key moments in science & technology

Tech

Keith Wicks

key moments in science &

nology

hamlyn

1
energy
6–17

2
materials
and
processes
18–27

46–55
farming and
fishing
5

56–71
transport
6

writing and
9 printing
92–99

100–109
photography
10 and the
cinema

13 126–135
medical
technology

14 weapons
136–145

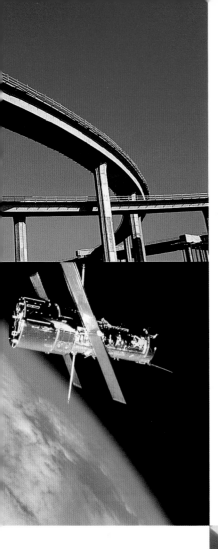

3 building and
construction
28–37

4 spinning
and
weaving
38–45

7 astronomy and
space exploration
72–83

84–91
measurements
8

110–117
domestic
appliances
11

recording
sound and
vision
118–125
12

15
communications
146–169

digital
computers
170–187
16

1

energy

Most of the energy we use comes from the Sun. Besides providing us directly with heat and light, the Sun also powers the process of photo synthesis, which enables green plants to grow. Radiant energy from the Sun ends up as chemical energy stored in the plants. These provide food for some animals and, indirectly, any predators. Coal, mineral oils and natural gas are fossil fuels, obtained from organisms that lived millions of years ago and depended on solar energy for growth. The wind is the result of weather systems, also powered by the Sun, and caused by uneven heating of the Earth's surface. And the weather brings rain and snow, which replenish the water flowing in streams and rivers. So the Sun is the ultimate source of almost all our energy, whether as heat, light, fuel, wind power, or water power, or as other forms of energy derived from them.

Fire

For early humans, most activities had to take place between sunrise and sunset, although night excursions were possible when there was sufficient moonlight. Fires started accidentally by lightning were useful, once man had learned to control and maintain the flames. This happened about 1.4 million years ago and, for the first time, heat and light became available throughout the night.

Methods of making fires were developed from around 7000 BC, and this simple technology must rate as the most important of all developments. In one method, rubbing the palms of the hands together rotated a small, vertical stick held between them. The lower, pointed end of the stick rested in a hole in another stick, and the friction there made it extremely hot. Eventually, it became so hot that particles of dry leaves or grass placed there would become red hot and, when blown on, would burst into flames and ignite larger pieces of grass and wood. Technically, fire making equipment like this is a friction machine that converts kinetic energy – energy of motion – into heat energy. And fire occurs when chemical energy stored in a fuel, such as wood, is converted into other forms of energy – heat and light.

Machines

One very early invention involving energy is very easy to overlook. To most people, a stick is just a stick but, if it is used as a lever, then a scientist would class it as a simple machine. If you place one end of a stick under a heavy stone, place a small stone close to the end to act as a pivot, and then press down on the stick to lever up the large stone, you are using the stick as a machine that provides a 'mechanical advantage'.

It might, for example, enable you to lift a stone weighing 100 kg by pressing down with a force of only 10 kg. As you might guess, you don't get something for nothing and, in this case, you would have to move the end of the stick about 10 cm for every centimetre that the stone moved. So, although the task is easier to carry out, you use about the same amount of energy as when lifting the load unaided. In fact, using a machine of any kind involves using more energy, because it takes energy to move the machine itself and overcome friction at the places where moving parts are in contact, and there may be other energy losses too.

previous An electricity substation, showing transformers that reduce the voltage for local use. Electricity is distributed around the country at high voltage because this reduces power losses in the cables.

left The bright lights of Piccadilly Circus in London are just one of the billions of end results of our use of energy.

The ratio of useful energy produced to total energy put in is called the efficiency of the machine. In the case of a machine that uses fuel, increasing the efficiency means that it will use less fuel to do a particular task, and the saving in running cost can make what was merely an interesting development into a useful machine.

Water power

If we use the term 'machine' in its more usual sense, then one of the first machines to be invented was the waterwheel. This dates back to at least the 1st Century BC, and was originally built so that the energy of moving water could be used to grind grain. In the undershot waterwheel, favoured by the Romans, the wheel was arranged with its lower part immersed in the stream. A gear coupled the horizontal axle of the large wheel to a vertical shaft, which turned a millstone. This was the first use of gear wheels, and the ratio of teeth was chosen according to the flow of the stream in order to provide a suitable grinding speed. Natural streams and rivers powered most waterwheels but, by 1100 AD, some millponds had been dug in coastal areas to trap tidal water for turning the machines.

The overshot waterwheel was a later design in which the stream of water was directed onto the upper part of the wheel. In the mid-1700s, English engineer John Smeaton made a study of waterwheels and found that the overshot wheel had an efficiency of more than 60 per cent, compared with little more than 20 per cent for an undershot wheel. However, French engineer Jean-Victor Poncelet streamlined the design of the undershot wheel in the early 1800s, making it even more efficient than the overshot type. By this time, waterwheels were widely used to provide power in many industries, which had been established along the banks of fast flowing streams and rivers.

above left Constructing a waterwheel at Burden Lake, Troy, New York, in 1919. Waterwheels have harnessed the energy of streams and rivers for more than 2,000 years, originally for grinding grain, then for powering various machines.

above The Kurobe Dam at Toyama, in Japan's North Alps, where water power is harnessed to generate electricity. Water from the reservoir is allowed to flow down and turn turbines, which are linked to electricity generators.

Wind power

The invention of sails, more than 6,000 years ago, enabled boats to travel long distances with relatively little manual labour. Sails were also used by the 7th Century AD to power windmills for grinding grain. These early mills, developed in Persia, had the sails mounted on a vertical shaft inside an enclosure, with an inlet and outlet to direct the airflow. The post mill, with exposed upright sails on a roughly horizontal shaft, was used in Europe from the late 1100s. A long pole extended from the back of the mill, which was pivoted on a sturdy post. The pole was used as a lever to swing the whole mill around when necessary so that the sails caught the wind. In the later tower mill, only a small part bearing the sail assembly had to be turned. English inventor Edmund Lee found a way to eliminate this task in 1745, when he devised the fantail – a set of vanes that caught the wind and orientated the sails automatically.

The wind is a less reliable source of energy than water, and so windmills were more suited to applications where a continual source of power was unnecessary, and where they could be left unattended. One important use was for operating pumps for irrigation and drainage.

below Wind power was used for centuries to drive such machines as windmills and pumps for raising water. More recently, wind farms, consisting of numerous huge rotors, called wind turbines, turn electricity generators so that the power can be stored for later use.

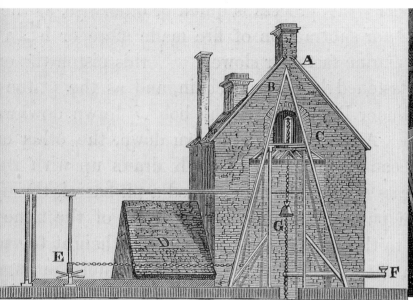

above James Watt studying a model of the steam engine that Thomas Newcomen had designed in about 1710. This engine was extremely inefficient because its cylinder was repeatedly heated and then allowed to cool to condense the steam in it. Watt devised a superior steam engine in the 1760s. It had a separate chamber for condensing the steam, so the cylinder could retain its heat.

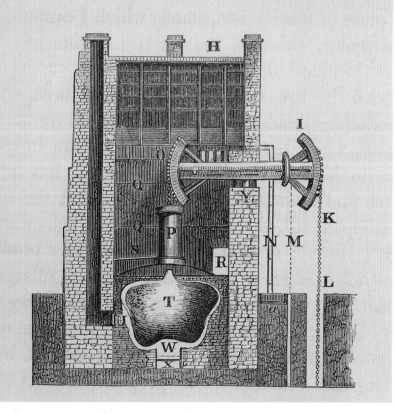

left The steam engine invented by Thomas Newcomen in the early 1700s and installed above a mine at Pool in Cornwall, England. The expansion and contraction of steam in the cylinder pushed the piston up and down. The piston rocked the arm at the top, which operated a pump for removing water from the mine.

above The electricity generators in this power station are driven by steam turbines, in which steam pressure produces rotary motion directly. The first practical steam turbine was invented in 1831 by American engineer William Avery.

Steam power

The first steam engine was a small steam turbine, invented by a Greek, Hero of Alexandria, in the 1st Century AD. Water was boiled in a sealed cooking pot, with tubes to take the steam into the sides of a hollow sphere, pivoted at the points where the tubes entered. The steam was allowed to escape through two small bent tubes at opposite sides of the sphere. As the jets of steam escaped, they made the sphere rotate. This is described as a turbine because it produces rotary motion, but Hero's aeolipile, as it was known, had little in common with the kind of turbines used today. The force of each jet produced an equal and opposite force on the sphere, in accordance with the third of Newton's laws of motion, formulated in the 1600s. The aeolipile was merely an interesting novelty and had no practical use, but it did demonstrate that steam could be used to produce continuous movement.

In the 1670s, French physicist Denis Papin invented a pressure cooker. The pressure of the steam was sometimes sufficient to force up the lid of the container, and this gave him the idea of using steam to move a piston. Papin's work later helped inspire others to build practical steam engines.

English engineer Thomas Savery invented the first practical steam engine in 1698. This was a form of pump, used for removing water from mines. Interestingly, Savery's machine did not have a piston. A metal chamber was filled with steam from a boiler, and then sprayed with cold water. This condensed the steam back into a small volume of liquid, thus reducing the pressure inside the chamber. The partial vacuum produced sucked water from the mine and into the chamber. More steam was piped into the chamber, forcing out the water, and the whole process was then repeated, the flow of water and steam being controlled by valves.

Thomas Newcomen, another English engineer, invented an improved steam engine around 1710. This used Papin's idea of having a piston moving in a cylinder. Newcomen and Savery formed a partnership and built the pump in 1712. After steam had pushed the piston up the cylinder, the cylinder was cooled with water and the partial vacuum produced inside allowed the external atmospheric pressure to force the piston back down. The process was then repeated, and the up-and-down movement of the piston operated a conventional mine pump.

Although better than Savery's pump, Newcomen's engine was very inefficient because a great deal of heat was lost each time the cylinder was cooled, and it had to be reheated before steam could be admitted again. John Smeaton later doubled the machine's efficiency but it could still only convert one per cent of the steam's energy into useful work.

Scottish inventor James Watt solved this problem in the 1760s by adding a separate condensation chamber for the steam, thus allowing the cylinder to be kept at a high temperature. This made the engine four times as efficient as the original model. Watt then teamed up with manufacturer Matthew Boulton and, assisted by engineer William Murdock, developed piston-operated steam engines that produced rotary motion for driving a wide range of industrial equipment. By the early 1800s, these steam engines were also being used to power ships, carriages, and locomotives and, in 1831, American engineer William Avery invented the practical

steam turbine, which used steam to turn a rotor instead of moving a piston. Steam engines played such an important part in the development of many industries that the 1800s become known as the age of steam.

Coal

The mechanical energy produced by steam engines comes ultimately from the fuel used to convert the water into steam. In most places, the easiest fuel to obtain used to be wood. Coal started to form from the remains of forests some 400 million years ago, and may have been first used as fuel by the Chinese around 1000 BC. In some places, outcrops were discovered, and mining started when the brittle rock was found to be such a good fuel. It took longer to light than wood, but burnt for longer and gave out more heat.

Coal mining in Europe started in the 1200s, and the gradual switch from wood to coal began in factories and homes. As underground workings became deeper, ventilation and safety measures had to be improved. Caged birds were taken down the mines as they needed plenty of oxygen, and a sick bird was usually a warning that the miners were in danger too. Coal seams sometimes gave off methane gas, known to miners as firedamp, and a miner's oil lamp could ignite it, causing an explosion and loss of life. In 1813, English chemist Humphry Davy invented a safety lamp that would not ignite the gas. Metal gauze around the flame conducted heat away so that the surface temperature was below the ignition point of the gas. This was not the first safety lamp to be invented, but it was the most successful, and saved countless lives. When

above left Humphry Davy testing his miner's safety lamp in the early 1800s. A metal gauze around the flame conducted heat away so that any methane gas in the mine would not be ignited. Until the safety lamp was introduced, occasional gas explosions were inevitable.

left A coal processing plant in operation. A wide range of products are made from coal. Heating coal in the absence of air produces coke and coal gas. This process also yields tar, light oil and ammonia, and from these are made a wide range of products, including fertilizers, dyes and drugs.

miners started using electric lamps in the early 1900s, they still had to have a safety oil lamp nearby because it acted as a warning device, the flame lengthening in the presence of methane.

Coal gas

Gas for lighting was originally manufactured by heating coal, the other main products from this process being tar and coke. Many people sitting by a fire must have seen burning jets of gas coming from the hot coals and wondered about extracting the gas. Experiments with coal gas lighting were carried out by various individuals from the 1600s, but it was not until 1807 that central London's Pall Mall became the first public street to have gas lighting. It was installed by a German called F A Winsor. Within 25 years, most of the large cities in Europe and the United States also had gas lighting in their streets. Domestic gas lighting became popular much later in the century, and later people started using it for heating and cooking too.

Oil and gas

Mineral oils and natural gas, like coal, were formed in the ground from deposits millions of years old – in this case, the remains of tiny aquatic plants and animals. Oil and gas reaches the surface in places, and some such oil was used for lighting and other purposes by ancient civilizations. The Chinese had the first oil wells in the 300s BC, but these were quite shallow and yields were poor. Oils, together with fats, have also been obtained since ancient times from animals, fish and plants.

below An oil production platform in the North Sea. Offshore production began in the 1890s off the coast of California, and America owned most of the world's oil production platforms until the 1970s, when other countries stepped up production.

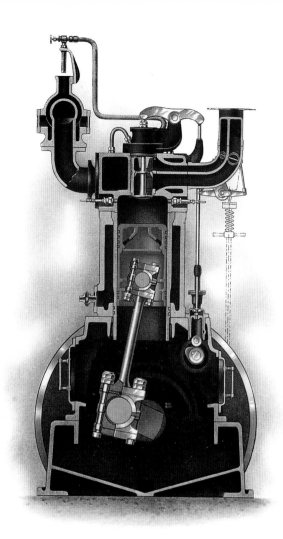

above A section through a single–cylinder internal combustion engine. Although most such engines run on petrol (gasoline) or diesel fuel, some have been designed to run on methane or hydrogen gas. As hydrogen is easily made by the electrolysis of water, this gas could be the future fuel for road vehicles.

The modern oil industry started in 1859, when railway worker Edwin Drake drilled the first successful oil well at Titusville, Pennsylvania, USA. While the region suddenly became rich, Drake lost his money by making bad investments, and he died in poverty. Others became multimillionaires, oil wells were established in other countries, and nearly 200 billion barrels of oil were produced in the industry's first hundred years. Originally, the crude oil (petroleum) was used for making paraffin (kerosene) for lamps. The petrol (gasoline) obtained was discarded as it was considered too dangerous to be used, but this has since become the main fuel used by road vehicles.

Natural gas, consisting mostly of methane and ethane, is often found with oil deposits. In some places, the gas escapes at the surface, and may be ignited. Such fires featured in ceremonies of the ancient Persians. By 200 BC, the Chinese were drilling for natural gas, which they burnt to dry salt that they had mined.

For centuries, natural gas was used locally, as there was no economic way of transporting it over long distances to other areas. Even when the oil industry started, any gas found was usually burnt off as there were no facilities for using it. Pipeline technology improved from the 1890s with the introduction of leakproof couplings, and long-distance pipelines were established from the late 1920s, enabling the natural gas industry to expand. Many countries have now changed from coal gas to natural gas for lighting and heating.

Electricity

Steam power still plays a vital role, as most or our electricity is produced by generators turned by steam turbines. The heat required to turn the water to steam may be produced by burning conventional fuels, or it may come from a nuclear reactor.

In the 1930s, Italian physicist Enrico Fermi was experimenting with nuclear fission – the splitting of an atom's nucleus. He found that, when he bombarded uranium-235 nuclei with neutrons, more neutrons were produced in the fission process, and these could cause a chain reaction in which further nuclei were split. At each stage, heat was given off and, if unchecked, this would cause the uranium to explode with devastating force, as predicted by Albert Einstein's Special Theory of Relativity. But, with careful control, the reaction could be made to release useful amounts of heat from just a small quantity of uranium fuel. Working in Chicago, Fermi successfully ran the first reactor for obtaining energy from nuclear fuel in December 1942.

The use of nuclear energy was predicted to bring cheaper electricity, and hope for the future when fossil fuel supplies run out. However, the operating costs of nuclear power stations have proved to be higher than expected, and radioactive waste has to be stored for long periods until harmless. Also, there is always the risk of an accident resulting in the release of radioactive substances. For these reasons, about 90 per cent of the energy used by the world's industrialized nations today still comes from fossil fuels, and alternatives to nuclear energy are sought.

Panels of solar cells, which generate electricity from solar radiation (mainly light), while convenient for spacecraft and used on some buildings, are too expensive for general use, although prices may be lower in the future. And schemes to harness tidal power have had limited success. As a result, the main development in recent years has been a new approach to an old idea – using turbines turned by the wind to generate electricity.

top Michael Faraday came from a poor family with little education, yet was one of the greatest scientists of the 1800s, inventing the electric motor and generator– forerunners of todays electrical machines.

right The turbine hall in the nuclear power station at Chooz, France. As in conventional power stations, steam turns the turbines, but the heat required to boil the water is obtained from nuclear fission reactions, instead of by burning coal, oil or gas.

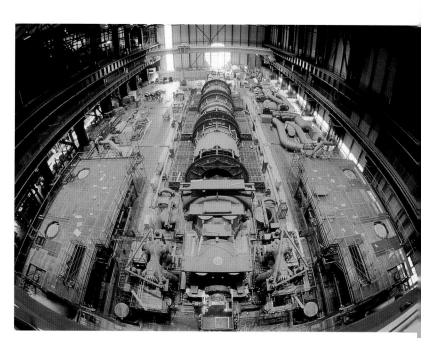

2

materials

and

processes

Inventions and discoveries are made in two distinct ways. Prolific American inventor Thomas Alva Edison attributed what some considered to be his genius mostly to hard work — 'one per cent inspiration and 99 per cent perspiration' — and countless inventors have devoted much of their lives to searching for solutions, quite often without success, and frequently with little or no reward. And yet, some major advances have been made as a result of chance discoveries. Such were the discoveries that enabled early man to smelt ores and, later, to make tools and weapons of bronze and leave behind his Stone Age existence.

Casting in copper

The Bronze Age followed the Stone Age, and started around 3500 BC but, by then, other metals had been used for about 1000 years. These were gold, silver and copper, all of which were found in the metallic state. People used stone tools to beat lumps of these metals into sheets and other forms. Small pieces of gold, such as small nuggets found in rivers, could also be combined into larger lumps by beating, and the same could

previous A moulded plastic bottle coming off the production line. Since the 1850s, various kinds of plastic have been introduced, and these have replaced wood, glass, metal and other materials in many manufacturing processes.

below A continuous-casting steel mill. The red-hot steel is pulled from the bottom of a mould while its core is still molten. A computer uses data from sensors to match the input of liquid steel to each mould with the speed of withdrawal.

be done with silver, whereas fragments of copper were extremely difficult to combine in this way. But then it was discovered that copper could be melted in a very hot fire and, if heated in a clay container, the metal could be shaped by pouring it into a mould of sand, clay or stone. The ability to make copper tools and weapons by casting was of great significance, although the metal was relatively scarce at first, and so production was limited. The first cast copper implements were made in Egypt around 4000 BC, but the precise date is uncertain because so few of these early copper items have survived. Copper is a relatively soft metal and, although casting made it harder, it also resulted in a rather brittle form that was more liable to fracture and, when items became damaged, they were put in the melting pot so that the scarce metal could be reused.

Smelting

The chance discovery that was of such great importance to mankind occurred around 3500 BC in Mesopotamia, when molten copper was seen coming from a hard mineral that had become mixed with hot charcoal in a fire. The heat had caused the charcoal to combine with substances in the mineral, copper ore, reducing it to metallic copper. As if by a miracle, this smelting process had provided people with a new source of the metal, and no doubt almost every other kind of mineral was soon being heated with charcoal in an attempt to discover more metals – occasionally with success.

Bronze Age

Bronze was probably first formed when some tin ore was accidentally added to copper ore during smelting. The resulting metal, combining copper and tin, was of such significance that the following period became known by the name of this first alloy – bronze. It proved to be extremely hard and strong, and was also resistant to corrosion, making it suitable for many purposes. The properties of the bronze could be modified by varying the proportions of copper and tin and, later, other metals were sometimes added too. The hardest bronze, for example, contains up to 25 per cent of tin, and a small proportion of lead. The Bronze Age started around 3000 BC, but occurred more than a thousand years later in some regions, although others never went through this stage of development, moving straight from Stone Age technology to that of the Iron Age.

Iron and steel

People continued to use various stone implements throughout the Bronze Age, and bronze tools were common long after iron came into production. The smelting of iron ore was first carried out in the Middle East around 2500 BC, but little ore had been discovered at that time, so the metal was regarded as precious, and not a material for common use. The Iron Age is the period from about 1300 BC, when supplies had become plentiful, and iron products relatively cheap. Blacksmiths shaped and joined the red-hot metal by hammering, and also discovered the technique of case-hardening. Heating an iron article in charcoal gave it a surface that could be made much harder by sudden cooling in water. This

below A robotic welding machine making machines for textile manufacture. Robots are ideally suited to performing such repetitive tasks, and can work for long periods without a break. Pipes remove the fumes to prevent pollution.

made it particularly suitable for weapons, tools, and machines, as well as for other less demanding purposes.

Higher quality iron was produced as techniques improved, notably the introduction of bellows to improve air flow to the fire of the furnace so that a higher temperature was attained. The first blast furnaces appeared in Europe in the 1300s and resulted in greatly increased production. The ore and charcoal were fed into the top of a shaft furnace, and air was blasted in at the bottom. From the 1600s, coke started to replace charcoal as the source of carbon.

Steel is an alloy, the main constituents being iron and carbon. Some forms of steel were first made in small quantities more than 2000 years ago, but modern steel making started in the mid-1800s, when English engineer Henry Bessemer introduced an economic technique and invented a steel making furnace which became known as the Bessemer converter. A similar technique was devised at about the same time in the USA by William Kelly. An improved method, called the open-hearth process, was introduced in the 1860s and, by the mid-1900s, had almost completely replaced the Bessemer process. Today, most steel is made by the faster basic-oxygen process, which is much more economic than the open-hearth process because it uses relatively little fuel.

Rubber

South American Indians were probably the first to obtain latex from certain trees and use it to make a form of rubber. They dipped their feet in the milk-like fluid so that, when it dried, it formed well-fitting and waterproof shoes. They also spread latex on cloth to make waterproof material for tents and clothing. And, farther north, the Aztecs are known to have had rubber balls in the 1400s. The solid material became known as rubber in the 1700s after English scientist Joseph Priestley said he found it good for rubbing out pencil marks.

Scottish chemist Charles Macintosh and English inventor Thomas Hancock were the first to appreciate the great importance of rubber. In the 1820s, Macintosh dissolved rubber in naptha and used it to glue two layers of cloth together, thus forming the first non-sticky waterproof material, and this was soon used in waterproof coats bearing his name. Hancock, who had become Macintosh's partner, produced elastic for garments, and a machine for recombining rubber offcuts.

The first rubber products changed character, depending on the temperature, becoming hot, sticky and smelly in summer, and hard and brittle in winter. American Charles Goodyear solved this problem in 1839, when he introduced the process of vulcanization, in which sulphur was combined with the rubber. This made the rubber more stable and much harder, enabling it to be used in various machines and, most importantly, for vehicle tyres. When the automobile industry started its rapid expansion around 1900, new plantations were established in Ceylon and Singapore in order to cope with the demand. When most supplies of natural rubber became cut off from the USA during World War II, chemists quickly established methods of producing synthetic rubber. Today, over half the rubber produced is synthetic.

right Assembly-line workers putting the finishing touches to tyres before despatch. Rubber was unsuitable for making tyres until Charles Goodyear introduced the process of vulcanization to make the material hard and stable.

Glass

Lightning sometimes strikes a beach, and the sudden burst of intense heat fuses the sand to produce a kind of glass. Pieces of glass that form when volcanic lava solidifies rapidly are known as obsidian. Some prehistoric people used this material to make arrowheads, tools, mirrors and ornaments. Glass making probably dates from the 4th Millennium BC, when it was used as a glaze on ceramics. The Egyptians developed a technique for making glass containers around 1500 BC. Using an iron rod, a worker would pull out a thread of molten glass and quickly wrap it around a clay former. In the 1st Century BC, the Phoenicians became the first people to use the technique of glass blowing. They used hollow iron rods to pick up a blob of molten glass and then blew it into shape. Sometimes this was done inside a former. The basic ingredients were readily available and were the same as used in common soda glass today – sand (silica, or silicon dioxide), soda (sodium carbonate) and lime (calcium oxide).

By this time, techniques for producing decorative pieces of glassware were well developed, metal oxides being used as colouring agents. Window glass first appeared in the 1st Century AD, but this was of poor quality, and difficult to see through clearly. The Romans made window glass by casting glass in slabs, but the resulting rough surface needed considerable polishing. In the Middle Ages, window glass was made by first blowing a sphere, then converting it into a disc. The resulting pane had a thickened 'bull's eye' in the middle, with distinct circles around it. Later, window glass was made by blowing an elongated shape, and then cutting out and flattening a pane. From the early 1900s, most sheet glass was made by dipping the end of a steel mesh into molten glass and using it to pull out a sheet between cooled rollers. This glass still had to be ground and polished afterwards. In the modern float process, invented by Alastair Pilkington in 1959, sheet glass is allowed to solidify on the surface of molten tin.

Glass is now available in thousands of forms, perhaps the most unusual being glass fibre. When drawn out into extremely fine threads, glass is so flexible that it can be woven to make fabric. Thick glass fibre matting is used for heat insulation. GRP is glass reinforced plastic, a very rigid laminate formed from glass fibre material and plastic. Products made from this material include boat hulls and baths.

above A porcelain workshop in Sèvres, near Versailles, France. Porcelain is a form of pottery that is usually translucent. The three main types are hard-paste (true) porcelain, soft-paste (artificial) porcelain, and bone china.

above left Glass blowing in a workshop in Brooklyn, New York City, in 1876. Although most glassware is now mass produced, some decorative items are still made by craftsmen using traditional methods.

left Glass bottles passing along a production line. Iron moulds rise and clamp around gobs of molten glass deposited through a tube. Air is then admitted to blow the glass into shape.

above An inspector checking the quality of a plastic bottle on a production line. Such containers are produced by the process of blow-moulding. Air or steam is used to blow a plastic resin into the shape of a surrounding mould.

Plastics

In the 1850s, English chemist Alexander Parkes made a new, hard, flexible material from a mixture of castor oil and chloroform. This first manufactured plastic, a form of cellulose nitrate, became known as Parkesine or Xylonite, and could be shaped by casting or stamping. For his achievement, Parkes was awarded a medal in 1862, but the new material aroused little interest. Two years later, American John Hyatt altered the process by substituting camphor for castor oil, and called his new plastic celluloid. This eventually became widely used with the expansion of the photographic and film industries around the turn of the century.

By the early 1900s, various other plastics had been devised, mostly made by modifying cellulose, obtained from wood pulp, but the material most remembered came in 1909, when Belgian-born American inventor Leo Baekeland reacted formaldehyde with phenol (carbolic acid) to produce an entirely new kind of plastic, which he called Bakelite. This was hard and, once formed, would not melt. It resisted burning, was a good electrical insulator, and appeared at just the right time for use in the expanding electrical appliance industry.

Theoretical work by German chemist Hermann Staudinger in the 1920s enabled others to understand the long-chain molecular structures of plastics and to develop many new materials.

Nanotechnology

Even if chemists know the chemical structure they need for a new material, it may prove impossible to produce by ordinary chemical processes. Nanotechnology is concerned with building materials by manipulating individual molecules and atoms, and should provide a way of manufacturing many new products. Because molecules and atoms are so small, it would take a considerable time to produce just one cubic centimetre of new material if this process of construction were carried out at a steady rate. The trick is to construct self-replicating assemblers – molecular structures that can build copies of themselves. This is taking a leaf from nature's book, as it resembles the way that organic material grows from cells. And, after a considerable sum has been spent on development costs, the price per assembler will be close to zero, because of its self-replication capability.

To show what can be achieved in small-scale structures, individual atoms in materials have been arranged to form letters, and a steam engine with overall dimensions smaller than the thickness of a human hair has been demonstrated. Promises for the future include robots that can be injected into the blood stream to clean up partially blocked arteries, and the development of microscopic computers.

Interest in nanotechnology came about following theoretical work in the USA by physicist and Nobel Laureate Richard Feynman and, later, by physicists Eric Drexler and Ralph Merkle. Although, not so long ago, some scientists thought nanotechnology to be a joke, it is now forecast to become a major development of the 21st Century and the trigger for a new industrial revolution.

below The amazing size of the microengines developed in the field of nanotechnology is illustrated in this image of the legs of a spider mite – a miniscule insect virtually invisible to the human eye – standing on a mirror drive assembly.

bottom The world's smallest microsteam engine. Water inside the compression cylinder – seen here in the centre – is heated by an electric current and vapourizes, pushing the piston out. Capillary forces retract the piston as the current is removed.

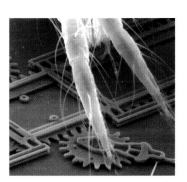

27 materials and processes

3

building and
construction

previous Spectacular view of a modern motorway 'cloverleaf' type junction under construction.

above Conical mud huts at Buniamin, Syria. Mud huts were one of the earliest forms of dwelling, and have been built in this region for thousands of years.

left The stone block construction can be seen clearly in the largest and most celebrated group of ancient Egyptian pyramids at Giza, built during the 4th Dynasty more than 2,500 years before Christ.

Most early buildings were made from local materials that could be shaped using simple tools. A wide range of materials came to be used, including ice in the Arctic, branches from the forests, skins from animals, and turf, stones, mud and clay from the ground. If necessary, these materials were generally shaped during construction of the dwellings. By about 6000 BC, an important development had occurred in Mesopotamia. Builders had started to make bricks from clay, shaped into slabs and left to dry in the sun. These easily handled units were mostly made in standard sizes for convenience, although special shapes were produced when required.

At first, mud was used for mortar but, by about 4000 BC, some builders were using a stronger bitumin mortar to hold brick structures together. Early bricks were quite weak by modern standards, but it was discovered that they became much tougher after heating to a high temperature near a fire. The heat bound together the particles in the material, making the resulting bricks less liable to crack under stress. And so, from about 3500 BC, methods of manufacturing fired bricks were adopted and gradually improved, and the technology gradually spread to other areas.

By this time, the development of bronze tools was enabling builders to make better use of materials. Axes were available to fell trees, and saws to cut them into planks for various types of construction. Tools were also developed for shaping and polishing stone, which became a most important building material in places where there were few trees. However, the material was so difficult to quarry and transport, and took so long to transform into a usable material, that it was generally reserved for special buildings and monuments.

The Egyptians first used large stone blocks for pyramids and temples built around 2600 BC. Bearing in mind the limited facilities available, the successful quarrying of materials and construction of the monuments involved great ingenuity and was an almost miraculous achievement. A block of softer, sedimentary rock, such as limestone, was extracted by first cutting vertically around it with a pick. Then horizontal holes were made in the block using a drill turned manually by a string held taut in a bow. Wooden pegs were hammered tightly into the holes and then allowed to absorb water. This made the pegs expand, and the forces produced were sufficient to split the stone away at the base. With harder rock, such as granite, extraction was usually assisted by the cruder technique of using another rock, shaped into a ball, to smash sections away. Once the blocks had been freed, they were transported overland by slaves or animals. There were no wheeled vehicles, so the blocks, each weighing up to 1,000 tonnes, had to be dragged along. Fortunately, the Egyptians had boats that could carry heavy loads, so stones that had to be transported over long distances were usually taken some of the way by river. After final preparation of the blocks, there remained the task of placing each one in its required position. This was done by dragging the blocks up temporary ramps and using simple levers to force the stones into place. Usually, a layer of gypsum mortar was placed between the blocks, but this is unlikely to have contributed much in the way of strength or stability. Their weight alone was enough to ensure that the blocks would stay where they were placed.

Roman influences

Stone is an extremely hard and durable material, but it has one major disadvantage. It can support enormous loads when these compress the material, but it cannot withstand large forces that produce tension. So it is fine for use in columns, where the load presses downwards, but has limited use as lintels for bridging large openings in structures. In such cases, the load above tends to bend the lintel down in the middle, so the top surface is compressed, while the underneath is stretched. This tension on the underside can lead to cracks and sudden collapse. The solution to the problem is to bridge the gap using an arch, which can be regarded as a lintel curved upwards in the middle.

Arches were used to a limited extent by the ancient Egyptians and Greeks, but the Romans were the first to fully exploit this most useful structure. Besides being suitable for spanning large gaps, it was also easy to construct from separate stones, so there was no single massive weight to manipulate into place.

The Romans had adapted their construction techniques to include brickwork, and they started to use bricks as well as stones for arch construction. They originally bound their bricks together with a lime mortar, but the rain tended to wear this away and they changed to a more durable mixture containing lime, volcanic ash and sand. Later, they added gravel to this mortar to make concrete. When they rebuilt the Pantheon in AD 123, they constructed for it an impressive brick and concrete dome measuring 43 metres across.

Concrete was less attractive than polished stone, but exposed sections were often clad with thin slices of decorative stone or brick, or with glazed tiles. Like stone, concrete had great strength in compression, but had the disadvantage of being relatively weak when under tension.

The Romans introduced their building techniques to other parts of Europe, resulting in brick becoming a popular building material. However, many of the ancient cities were already a fire hazard, as many buildings were made of wood, and they were built close together too. Disaster came to London in September 1666, when the capital experienced its worst fire. It destroyed more than 13,000 houses, over 80 churches, and St Paul's Cathedral. Under the supervision of Christopher Wren, rebuilding after the great fire made extensive use of brick to ensure that no such large-scale disaster could ever happen again.

above A 1787 painting of Le Pont du Gard by Hubert Robert. This Roman aqueduct carries water over the Gard river to Nîmes, in the south of France. It was built in about 19 BC. The painting now hangs in the Louvre Museum, Paris.

above This Roman aqueduct, built in the 100s AD, in the reign of Emperor Trajan, is still used to carry water to the town of Segovia, near Madrid, in central Spain. This is the largest remaining Roman structure in the country.

above American inventor Elisha Otis, who demonstrated the safety of his elevator (lift) in 1852 by standing on it while the supporting cable was cut. The safety device worked, Otis lived, and passenger elevators became accepted by the public.

top A modern high-rise building project taking place in present-day Tokyo. The steel-frame construction can be seen clearly here.

Modern materials

Some aspects of building construction have hardly changed since Roman times. Many houses are still built brick by brick, in the traditional manner, although with materials of much improved quality. But other structures built today use more modern techniques and materials unavailable to the ancient builders. One of the most important developments occurred in the 1700s, when new processes had resulted in cheaper iron and steel becoming available. Iron was soon used for building bridges, railway stations and other structures.

Then, in 1867, a French gardener called Joseph Monier covered an iron mesh with concrete to make flowerpots. He had invented a form of reinforced concrete, and later suggested ways of using the composite material in bridges and buildings. François Hennebique, also French, found that he could incorporate iron bars into concrete slabs to give the material strength in tension as well as in compression. The resulting reinforced concrete could be used in applications where slabs of ordinary concrete would break down, thus greatly increasing its usefulness. It also removed some of the restrictions that architects had previously experienced, allowing them to design structures impossible to construct with the materials previously available. Notable among these new kinds of structures was one of Hennebique's own designs – the three-arch Vienne River bridge, built at Châtellerault, France, in 1899. This was the longest

above A view over Manhattan, New York City, from the Empire State Building. Skyscrapers were made possible by the steel-frame construction technique, and the invention of the safety elevator, which enabled people to reach the upper floors easily.

bridge built that century, the central arch alone spanning a distance of about 50 metres.

The availability of iron for construction also led to a trend that was eventually to change the face of cities throughout the world. In traditional buildings, the ground-floor walls have to support the entire load above. So, as buildings became higher, the walls at ground level had to be stronger, and that meant thicker, in order to support the load. There was clearly a limit to how tall a traditional building could be, because there was little point in adding stages to the top of the building if it meant that there would be inadequate space left on the lowest floors because of excessive wall thickness.

Another problem was that, even when a very tall building was constructed, people would not want to walk up so many stairs to the top. Lifts were already in use, mainly for carrying goods, but were generally considered to be too dangerous for carrying passengers. American engineer Elisha Otis removed the danger in the 1850s with the invention of his safety hoist for lifts. In a spectacular demonstration, he was lifted high into the air and then the rope was cut. His safety device arrested his fall, and the success of his invention was guaranteed. Soon, people would be riding in safety to the upper floors of buildings.

In 1885, a new kind of building appeared in Chicago. The ten-storey Home Insurance Building, Chicago, had an iron frame that supported the

above The construction of new roads requires heavy equipment to dig and shift large quantities of materials. The task is minimised to some extent by planning the route so that the material removed from high parts of the land is just sufficient for building up the lower parts.

top The A5 motorway in France under construction. In some countries, road construction is now being slowed down, and ways of encouraging alternative means of transport are being sought.

structure, so there was no need for thick walls. The metal frame and the safety lift, or elevator, had made the skyscraper possible, and led to the 100-floor-plus structures we see in cities today.

Roads and railways

The Romans were highly skilled at constructing roads with smooth surfaces, firm foundations, and a camber to ensure proper drainage. These roads, built mainly to facilitate military transport, and notable for their very long, straight sections, extended east-west from Mesopotamia to Britain, and north-south from the Black Forest to North Africa. After the fall of the Roman Empire, little maintenance was carried out, and many of these routes eventually disappeared altogether. But other parts formed the basis for today's highways across Europe.

In Britain, road building flourished again in the 1700s, when Scottish engineers Thomas Telford and John McAdam constructed new routes. McAdam contributed to the spread of the technology by publishing books on the subject, and he also introduced a revolutionary and economic surfacing material that was named after him – tarmacadam, or tarmac. Telford organized the building of over 1,600 km of roads as well as some 1,200 bridges.

By the early 1830s, road construction had almost ceased in Britain as so much money had been allocated to building a railway network, although some extra roads were built to service the new railway stations. Railways became more economic to maintain in the late 1850s, following the invention of the Bessemer converter for making mild steel. The old iron rails were replaced with the stronger steel rails, which needed replacing less often. With an increasing number of motor vehicles being produced around the turn of the century, investment in new road systems started again, leading eventually to the establishment of motorway systems in Europe and North America.

Bridges and tunnels

Early man sometimes found that trees had fallen across rivers and streams. Once a few branches had been removed, these natural bridges provided an easy means of getting across. A structure like this is a form of single-span beam bridge. If the distance to be spanned is too long, a

above Engineers assembling a boring machine in a tunnel in Taiwan. After a section has been cut away by the cutter's tungsten carbide teeth, the spoil is removed and a concrete ring is constructed to prevent the tunnel from collapsing.

top The world's first large iron bridge was built across the River Severn in Shropshire, England, in 1779. It was designed by Thomas Pritchard and withstood the 1795 floodwaters so well that many more bridges were soon made of iron instead of stone.

wooden beam sags in the middle and is likely to break, so extra supports have to be added, making it into a multi-span bridge. A stone beam cannot span a large gap either because, as with lintels used across large gaps inside buildings, the stress underneath tends to cause cracking and eventual failure. As in buildings, one solution is to use an arch instead of a flat beam. The arch bridge converts the downward forces into outward thrusts at the ends of the arch, which are kept in place by massive supports called abutments. The third main type of bridge is the suspension bridge, in which cables are usually fastened to towers that support the load.

The Romans made great use of the circular arch in their stone bridges. The world's first large iron bridge was the single-arch structure built in 1779 over the River Severn at Coalbrookdale, England. Suspension bridges date from ancient times, when vines were twisted together and used to support a narrow wooden track. The first modern suspension bridge was the work of Thomas Telford, who built it to link the island of Anglesey with the Welsh mainland in the 1820s.

The earliest tunnels were built in ancient times for access to minerals, water-bearing rocks, and tombs. A notable Roman project involved 30,000 slaves working over ten years to dig a tunnel 5 km long to drain a lake near Rome. Modern tunnelling started in the 1760s in England, so that canals could be routed through hills. The expertise gained was used in the following century for building railway tunnels. The labourers who built the original canal navigations were called 'navies', and this is still the term used for men who dig holes in the ground with picks and spades.

4

spinning

and

weaving

4

previous Silk threads being woven into cloth on a loom at Sengkang, Indonesia. As in most countries, high-speed powered looms have almost entirely replaced the traditional hand-operated type.

left A carved slab depicting a Hittite woman from the 7th or 8th century BC. She is carrying a wooden spindle, a device used since ancient times for spinning fibres into continuous thread.

John Kay (1704-1764)

English engineer John Kay invented the flying shuttle, which helped to automate the weaving process. A hand-operated mechanism threw the shuttle, carrying a weft thread, through the warp threads. Previously, two weavers passed the weft through by hand but, with the flying shuttle, a single weaver could carry out the task simply by tugging on a cord. Kay's shuttle also enabled a weaver to produce cloth of greater width than before.

Kay patented the flying shuttle in 1733. This labour-saving device

caused Kay a great deal of trouble, because it reduced the demand for weavers, who became worried that they would soon be out of work. Eventually, a mob of weavers drove Kay from his home in Colchester, Essex, and he retreated to his birthplace of Bury, Lancashire. However, another mob attacked his new home and, feeling unsafe in England, Kay went to France in 1747 and introduced the flying shuttle to the weaving industry there. He also invented various machines for use in the textile industry. Kay is presumed to have died in 1764, as nothing is known of him after that date.

As our hairy, ape-like ancestors gradually evolved to become smooth-skinned humans, some form of clothing became a necessity, especially in cooler climatic zones and winter months. Having killed animals for food, it was natural to use the remaining skins for keeping out the cold, and these gradually evolved into recognisable garments. Readily available materials were not ideal for all purposes, and so techniques were developed for making new kinds of materials. Two of the most important techniques were spinning and weaving.

According to archaeologists, people in what we now know as the Middle East were probably making simple woven mats from grass or reeds by about 7000 BC. Later, it was discovered that natural fibres, such as flax and wool, could be spun to make yarn of any length, and the yarn could be woven into cloth. The earliest known textiles are pieces of linen found in Egyptian tombs and dating from around 5000 BC.

In ancient Egypt, spinning was carried out using a wooden spindle with a stone or clay bowl-shaped flywheel at one end. The device was made to spin rapidly, like a child's top, so that the rotating spindle would twist together a mass of loose fibres.

The first hand-operated spinning wheel appeared around 500 BC in India and speeded up the process of making yarn. Known as the great wheel, it appeared in Europe in the Middle Ages, and another type called the Saxony wheel was invented in Germany around 1500. This was operated by hand, or by a pedal that was linked to the spindle by a drive belt, and the thread was drawn off by hand.

Simple weaving was originally done without the aid of machinery but, over the centuries, people found various ways of using beams and rods to hold and move an assembly of threads, called the warp, while another thread, called the weft, was passed through them. At first, most looms were operated by hand, but treadles were eventually introduced to leave the weavers' hands free for other tasks.

Kay's flying shuttle

In spite of various improvements in loom design, techniques changed very little until the dawn of Europe's Industrial Revolution. In the 1730s, an Englishman called John Kay invented a device called the flying shuttle. A weft thread inside the shuttle was released through a hole as the shuttle was thrown back and forth through the warp threads on the loom. The introduction of the flying shuttle had a dramatic effect on the textile industry, for it doubled the rate at which a weaver could work, and yarn makers could not keep up with the increased demand. As a result, inventors soon started trying to solve the problem by developing machines for high-speed spinning. Kay became involved in various lawsuits while trying to ensure that he benefitted from the royalties for his inventions. Unfortunately, whatever income he did receive, most of it seems to have gone to pay his lawyers' fees.

Spinning jenny

The first of the new spinning machines were unsuccessful, and it was more than 30 years before a breakthrough came. In 1764, English weaver

James Hargreaves invented a machine called the spinning jenny. The origin of the name is uncertain, but Hargreaves may have named the machine after a daughter. With the first such machine, installed at Brookside, Lancashire, one worker could turn a handle to make eight spindles spin eight threads of yarn at the same time, thus bringing about a great increase in output. The new machine was welcomed by the weavers, for an ample supply of yarn would enable their trade to flourish, but spinners took a different view. They saw the jenny as a threat to their future, as they felt that fewer workers would be employed. Feelings ran so high that, in 1768, a group of spinners set fire to the machines at the factory and to Hargreaves' home. He was forced to leave, but managed to established a successful textile business in Nottingham. Hargreaves increased the number of spindles on his machines to 16, and soon he was making machines with 26 spindles. Others increased the number to 120, and some machines were operated by foot instead of by hand. The main disadvantage of the yarn produced by the spinning jenny was that it was not strong enough to take the strain undergone by the warp threads in a loom, so it could be used only for the weft.

Hargreaves died ten years after he moved to Nottingham, a fairly prosperous man, but by no means as rich as he might have been. Unlike Kay, Hargreaves had not bothered to protect his invention, and others had been able to benefit from the increased production that the jenny brought without having to pay royalties.

Spinning frame

Richard Arkwright was another inventor from the north of England who turned his thoughts to devising machines for spinning yarn. The result was the spinning frame, which he patented in 1769. This produced a yarn superior to that made on a spinning jenny and was the first machine capable of spinning strong warp threads at high speed. Within two years, Arkwright and his business partners had established their first textile factory near Matlock, Derbyshire, and they went on to set up several more in the north. Arkwright first used horses to provide the power to turn machinery, but then set up his factories in places where there was reliable water power. Later still, he used steam engines, but his spinning machine retained its popular name – Arkwright's water frame.

Arkwright was more successful than Kay and Hargreaves, not because he was more inventive, but because he was a better businessman and understood factory production techniques and the importance of using powered machinery. By the 1780s, he was a major employer in the textile industry, and his achievements were further rewarded by a knighthood in 1786.

Crompton's mule

Samuel Crompton could see ways of improving the spinning jenny by incorporating some features of Arkwright's frame so that the yarn produced would be similar in quality to the hand-made product. The resulting machine, built in 1779 when Crompton was in his mid-20s, was known as the mule. It produced superb yarn at high speed, and became

below Weaving cotton on an industrial loom in the mid-1920s. The transition from hand-operated to powered looms started in the 1700s. Water power and steam power eventually gave way to the electric motor for driving looms.

the prototype on which numerous industrial cotton spinning machines were to be based. Although extremely inventive, Crompton was yet another who lacked the ability to establish a successful business. He failed to raise the money to patent his machine, and relied instead on promises of financial reward from manufacturers in return for his cooperation. But although his machine had been produced in large numbers, and every day millions of spindles were turning out yarn in the way he had devised, by the time Crompton was approaching the age of 60, he had received almost nothing. Then Parliament took pity on the man who had done so much for the British cotton industry and awarded him the sum of £5,000. This he invested in various business ventures connected with textiles – but with little success.

Advances in weaving

Arkwright's use of powered machinery for spinning inspired a visiting clergyman to construct his own powered loom. That visitor was Edmund Cartwright, who patented his first loom in 1785, only a year after his visit to Arkwright's factory. At first, Cartwright relied on people to power the loom, but it was such hard work that he produced a steam-powered model the following year. In 1791, worried weavers fearing for their jobs burnt down a mill that had placed a large order for Cartwright's power looms. But the workers had little to fear as Arkwright's machines were never very efficient. Cartwright also had his share of financial misfortune, having to hand over a factory to settle debts, but Parliament did vote to award him £10,000 in recognition of his efforts in starting to mechanise the weaving industry.

above Yarn being wound onto bobbins at a textile mill for use on looms. Shuttles carry bobbins of weft threads across the cloth while the warp threads are held apart.

right The mechanized harvesting of the cotton plant, which is grown for its fibres. These fibres, known as lint, are seed hairs. They are contained within a seed capsule called a boll. Some mechanical harvesters pull the fibres from the bolls, whereas other harvesters remove the whole bolls from the plants.

Joseph Marie Jacquard (1752-1834)

French weaver Jacquard perfected a system of using punched cards to control the operation of a loom. The device containing the cards is called a Jacquard attachment, or Jacquard mechanism. The Jacquard loom enables intricate patterns to be woven automatically and helped to revolutionise the textile industry in the early 1800s.

The Jacquard loom, which incorporated the ideas of several other inventors, was first demonstrated in 1804. It was so successful that it soon became widely used and, in 1806, the French government declared it public property, rewarding Jacquard with a pension. French silk workers in Lyon were less happy. Fearing that the new looms would make them redundant, they destroyed some of the equipment and assaulted Jacquard. However, the trouble eventually died down, and the government presented Jacquard with a gold medal, and made him a member of the Légion d'Honneur.

Patterns

Simple looms are inconvenient for weaving highly complex patterns because various groups of warp threads have to be lifted together before the wefts are threaded through. The complex drawloom was developed for such tasks and had reached Europe by the Middle Ages. An operator called a drawboy had the task of pulling strings to control the lifting of the warps, but mistakes were often made and patterns spoiled. Somehow, human error had to be eliminated.

In France, Basil Bouchon introduced a form of what we would now call programming into pattern weaving in 1725. A moving band of paper with lines of coded perforations conveyed the pattern information to the loom. Rods associated with the warp strings rested against the paper, and passed through the holes from time to time. In this way, the pattern of holes ensured that specific warp-string rods were selected at each stage, thus eliminating errors.

With Bouchon's device, the loom still needed an assistant to pull the strings for the weaver. Twenty years later, Jaques de Vaucanson tried to find a way of eliminating the assistant altogether, but the mechanism he devised was too complex and never worked reliably. However, an improved version of Vaucanson's drawloom eventually appeared in 1804. This was the work of a weaver's son from Lyon called Joseph Marie Jacquard. Like the Vaucanson design, Jacquard's loom used punched cards to control the weaving patterns. Warp-thread selection was completely automatic, and complex patterns could be woven without error. Ever since that time, the punched-card pattern controlling mechanism used in looms has been know as the Jacquard attachment.

Colours

The use of dyes to colour textiles dates back to before 2000 BC but, until the mid-1800s, the only colouring agents available were natural dyes, obtained mostly from plants. Many of these pigments could be used directly on animal fibres, such as wool and fur, but were too easily washed out of cotton and other plant fibres. This problem was overcome by first treating the fibres with metal compounds called mordants. These reacted with the dyes, forming new coloured substances that clung fast to the fibres. Altering the mordant could change the final colour produced by a dye because different products were formed in the reactions. A range of colours could therefore be obtained by using mixtures of mordants in various proportions. But some colours were more difficult to obtain than others, and there was a need for synthetic dyes that could be produced easily by chemical processes.

The English chemist William Perkin accidentally produced the first synthetic dye in 1856, when he was experimenting with the coal-tar product aniline. At the time, he was trying to synthesise the drug quinine, but realized the importance of the blue-purple material he had made. It became known as mauveine, and its discovery led to the start of the synthetic dyestuffs industry. Perkin started commercial production of this dye the following year, and other chemists found ways of making dyes of other colours. Their initial approach was to study natural dyes and

attempt to reproduce them in the laboratory, but then completely new synthetic dyes were produced, having no natural counterparts. An important dye first produced in 1884 was congo red, the first dye that gave satisfactory results when applied directly to cotton.

Today, thousands of dyes are available, the majority of them produced synthetically. Different materials often require different kinds of dye so, if a fabric contains a mixture of fibres, it may be necessary to use a combination of dyes in order to colour it properly.

Printed Patterns

Printing patterns onto cloth may have been carried out first in India in the 300s BC. For centuries, the traditional method was to apply a dye or other colouring substance to a printing block and press this directly onto the material. In modern textile printing, there are two main alternatives to the direct approach. In the resist process, the cloth is printed with a substance that protects it from the dye, which is then applied to colour the rest of the material. In discharge printing, the cloth is first dyed to give it an overall colour. Then selected areas are removed by a chemical that is printed on in the form of a paste. Dyes resistant to the chemical may be applied with it in order to give the material a second colour. Although dyes are now available in a wide range of colours and types, the development of new fabrics and other materials continues to place demands on the chemical industry for even more ranges of dyes.

above Inspectors checking the quality of the coloured pattern on a textile. The pattern was applied by printing rollers (upper centre), each one applying a separate colour to build up the pattern in stages.

above left The dyers market in Fez, Morocco. Natural dyes, obtained mainly from plants, were used to colour cloth and other materials until the mid-1800s, when the first synthetic dye appeared. Most modern dyes are synthetic, and are produced from chemicals obtained from petroleum or coal.

farming and fishing

5

For humans, obtaining food was once a time consuming business involving regular expeditions to hunt animals, catch fish, or gather fruit, nuts, leaves, seeds and and other plant products. With simple weapons, such as spears and clubs, they could hunt larger animals too. All food was eaten raw, until the advantages of cooking were discovered when meat was left near a fire. Archaeological evidence from Kenya and South Africa suggests that man learnt to control and maintain fires more than 1,400,000 years ago. These were started accidentally by lightning, and methods of starting fires when required, using friction to generate heat, or flint to make sparks, were not discovered until around 8000 BC. Besides making meat more tender, roasting it over a fire also helped to preserve it for longer. By this time, potters were making vessels from clay, and these enabled even the toughest meat to be tenderised by boiling or stewing.

From time to time, local food resources became scarce, and tribes had to move on to other areas. Sometimes the hunters lit fires to drive out animals hiding in the forest, and the grass that eventually sprang up in the clearings attracted other animals. From about 8000 BC, people began to see that, with planning, they could settle in an area and obtain all the food they needed by raising crops and animals. Grain, sheep, goats, pigs and cattle were the most important products of these pioneer farmers.

After burning down trees, farmers found that the crops they grew on the land were improved if the wood ash had been dug into the ground. Seeds were sown in holes made by sticks, or were simply trodden into the soil by man or animals. Sometimes a stick was dragged through the ground to break up the soil before planting crops, and this led to the development of the plough. Besides making it easier to plant seeds, tilling the soil also produced a better crop, although the reasons for this were unknown at the time. In fact, exposure to the air promoted the release of plant nutrients from organic matter, and the plant roots could take up oxygen more easily too.

The most successful settlements were established in the valleys of great rivers, such as the Nile, where the soil was most fertile, and water was available for irrigation in times of low rainfall. By the 3rd Millennium BC, a wide range of farming activities were carried out by the Sumerians in the Tigris-Euphrates valley. Oxen pulled their wagons and also their ploughs, which were steadied and guided by a ploughman. Another draft animal used in Sumer was the wild ass. The horse was first domesticated in Asia around 4000 BC, and this replaced the ass in Sumer in about 2000 BC. By this time, particular types of cattle were recognised as being more suitable for milk or meat.

previous Rows of uncooked sausage rolls being fed into an oven on a conveyor belt. They take precisely the amount of time needed to cook them to travel through the oven.

left A wall painting from the tomb of Sennedjem in Dayr–al–Madinah (Thebes–West), Egypt, showing him ploughing the soil while his wife follows, sowing seed.

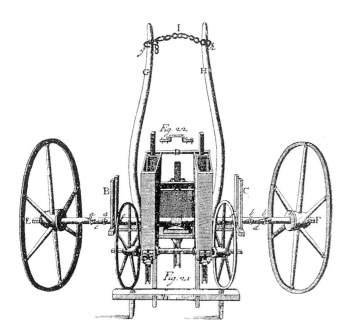

Jethro Tull (1674-1741)

Although he had studied law, and was called to the bar in 1699, Tull chose instead to take over from his father and operate the family farm in Oxfordshire, England. Tull had an inventive mind and, around 1701, he completed an automatic seed drill (above left) for sowing wheat in neat rows. This avoided the wastage that occurred when farmers scattered their seed by hand, and started the trend towards automation in agriculture.

Tull decided to plant crops in rows after spending a few years touring Europe. While in France, he visited vineyards, and noticed that the vines were planted in rows. In between, the earth had been broken up to allow air and water to reach the roots of the crops more easily.

Besides inspiring Tull to devise his seed drill, these observations led him to build horse-drawn hoes to break up the soil between rows of crops and keep down the weeds. This was so successful that Tull wrote a book about it called *The New Horse Houghing Husbandry: Or an Essay on the Principles of Tillage and Vegetation*. It was published in 1731 but, at first, few people believed that Tull's methods were worthwhile, and it was some years before farming benefitted from the widespread use of his techniques.

Roman agriculture

Similar developments in agriculture had taken place along the major river valleys in other countries, although the crops and animals varied from region to region, as did the quantities of food produced. The ancient Romans were unable to produce enough food to feed their people, so they had to import, among other things, fruit from the East and wheat from Egypt. To increase the yield of their own crops, the Romans produced large quantities of compost to spread on the land. They also allowed land to lie fallow for a year after harvesting, which allowed the nutrients in the soil to build up again before the next crop was planted. More importantly, they experimented with methods of crop rotation, by which one crop would enrich the soil with nutrients needed by the following crop. Suitable sequences of crops were found by trial and error, as they knew little about the science of the soil. The Romans brought these techniques, together with methods of irrigation and the use of oxen to pull the plough, to many countries in Europe.

Simple tools were used throughout agriculture until waterwheels and windmills were invented for grinding grain in order to make flour. The origins of these devices is obscure, but waterwheels first appeared in Roman times, around 100 BC, while windmills may have been invented in Persia in the 600s AD.

Horses were much faster than oxen for ploughing, but not so strong. To make matters worse, the harness restricted the animals' breathing by pressing on the windpipe, which hardly encouraged them to pull hard. The Chinese invented the padded horse collar, which overcame this problem by transferring the pressure to the animals' shoulders. This important invention reached Europe in the 1100s and resulted in a much greater use of the horse in agriculture, although oxen continued to work on the land too because they were relatively cheap to purchase and feed.

Agricultural Revolution

In Britain, the 1700s were the start of a period that became known as the Agricultural Revolution. Up to that time, farming was still carried out using tools and techniques that had been around for centuries. Then, new equipment and methods were gradually introduced, and these brought about widespread changes. For the introduction of machines reduced the demand for labour on the farms, and many people moved from the country to the towns to seek employment.

In the early 1700s, most farmers still planted their crops by scattering seed by hand. What farmers needed was a more efficient method that would place the seed where required and reduce waste. Around 1701, English lawyer Jethro Tull invented a horse-drawn machine for sowing seed in precise rows. The simple seed drill, consisting of a tube for depositing seed onto the soil while ploughing, had been invented in ancient times, but not generally adopted. Tull's machine worked automatically and, after initial resistance from farmers, the use of his drill gradually became more common, although more than a century passed before it was generally adopted. Tull also invented horse-drawn hoes for removing weeds from between the rows of crops.

below An early reaper, designed in 1826 by Scotsman Patrick Bell. It has many features found on modern harvesters. American Cyrus McCormick is usually credited with inventing the reaper because of his highly successful design of 1834.

left A combine harvester depositing grain into a storage truck. During harvesting, the machine's rotating paddlewheel pushes the crop against a cutting bar. After entering the harvester, the crop is threshed to release the grain.

below left An experiment in steam-powered ploughing, carried out by Lord Willoughby d'Eresby at Grimsthorpe, Lincolnshire, England, in 1861. A belt coupled the traction engine to a winding mechanism, which pulled the plough.

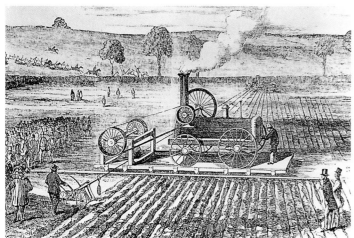

In England, former politician Charles Townshend introduced a new system of crop rotation that made it unnecessary to have any fallow land, and also produced winter feed for livestock. Until then, most livestock had to be slaughtered in the autumn. Being able to maintain the herd throughout the winter meant that fresh meat became available all year round. Townshend used turnips in his four-crop rotation system, and this earned him the nickname of 'Turnip' Townshend. Prominent landowner Thomas Coke promoted Townshend's system in the late 1700s, after it had greatly increased productivity on his own land, and the four-crop rotation system became established in the 1800s. As both Townshend and Coke both farmed in Norfolk, the method became known as the Norfolk system.

Another important new technique was intensive breeding, introduced by English farmer Robert Bakewell in the late 1700s. He improved livestock by breeding from parents selected for specific characteristics, and was particularly successful in developing the Leicester sheep. The lambs fattened very quickly, thus reducing the price that farmers had to charge for mutton, and making the meat a popular choice.

Mechanization

Cereals had always been a most important food, and so many inventors tried to develop machines to harvest and process the crop. Various threshing machines, for separating grain from the straw and husks, appeared in the late 1700s, but a more successful model was invented in the mid-1830s by American brothers Hiram and John Pitts. The first successful reaper, or harvesting machine, was a horse-drawn machine invented at about the same time by another American, Cyrus McCormick. The development of these machines led to the invention of a single machine that could carry out both reaping and threshing – the combine harvester, or combine. Although the first horse-drawn model was introduced in 1836, the combine did not become popular until the introduction of powerful tractor-hauled designs in the 1930s.

Around the turn of the century, horses were still widely used for pulling and powering farm machinery, but stationary steam engines had been used for some tasks from the early 1800s, and steam traction engines had been introduced in the 1870s. These powerful steam vehicles could haul very heavy loads, but they proved to be too slow and heavy for general farm use, and the smaller tractor, powered by an internal combustion engine, was replacing the traction engine on farms by 1900. From its beginning as a simple haulage vehicle, the farm tractor was developed into a highly versatile machine capable of hauling and controlling a wide range of farm equipment.

The first tractors were open vehicles, giving no protection from adverse weather conditions, and the driver could easily be crushed if the vehicle capsized on rough ground. Modern tractors provide much more comfort and security, having an air-conditioned and even soundproofed protective cab. In some modern farming systems, the tractors need no drivers, being under computer control, with an accurate navigation system to check their precise positions.

below Holstein–Friesian cows in a modern rotary milking parlour. The milk is drawn from the udder by means of a pulsating suction machine. An electronic tag identifies each animal so that its yield can be checked and recorded.

below For people who want something resembling a traditional meal, but don't have much time to spend in the kitchen, the packaged meal provides an answer. The foil trays of pre-cooked food just need to be warmed in an oven.

Modern techniques

Competition to produce cheap food of consistent quality has resulted in 'factory farming', with animals confined in small enclosures or crowded together so much that some are occasionally trampled to death. Modern chicken farms, for example, generally hold a few tens of thousands of birds, but the largest holds five million battery hens. Their droppings fall through their small wire cages, which are sloped so that the eggs roll to the front for collection. Chickens reared for meat are kept all together in large broiler houses.

Pigs may be conceived through artificial insemination, born through induced labour, weaned in half the natural time, and then have their feeding regulated by computers, which keep track of the animals by means of sensors that detect their electronic ear tags. Added to the feed are antibiotics, vitamins, and inorganic growth promoters. In addition, hormones produced by genetically engineered micro-organisms may be implanted or injected into the animals to bring them quickly up to weight for slaughtering.

Less has changed in general crop production, but artificial fertilizers are dug into the ground, and chemicals are sprayed to combat weeds, pests and plant diseases. Various products are modified using genetic engineering techniques to improve their appearance, flavour or other properties. Some crops are grown indoors by feeding their roots with a stream of water containing nutrients, a technique known as hydroponics. The roots may be suspended in the stream, or held in sand or plastic granules. Many salad products are grown this way, which avoids problems such as diseases from the soil, and the appearance of weeds. It also uses less water, because the vapour given off is collected and recycled. In the future, it may be economic for fish farms to cultivate plants in hydroponic units, using the waste matter from the fish as nutrients.

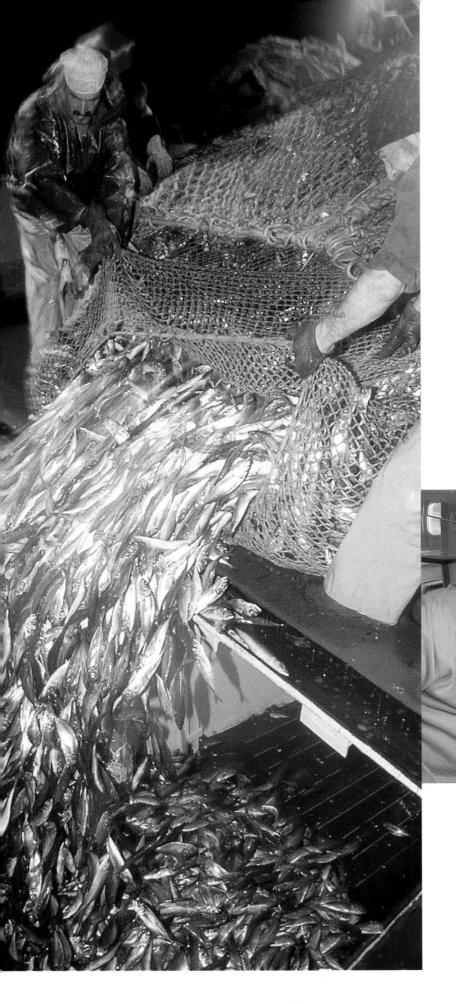

Fishing

Like the farmers, fishermen used traditional techniques for thousands of years, and only in recent times have major changes been made in methods of obtaining fish for food. People originally trapped, speared or netted just enough fish for their own needs but, when fishing became a major industry, much larger quantities were caught.

Fishing lines and nets increased in size when powered winches and other handling devices were installed on boats from the 1800s, and huge catches became common by the early 1900s. A great improvement came in the late 1940s, when rot-proof nets made of synthetic material replaced the old ones made of natural fibres. This period also saw the introduction of the first factory ships for processing the catch on board. Another development was the use of sonar systems to detect shoals of fish. After years of record catches, restrictions had to be imposed from the 1970s in order to ensure supplies for the future, and many factory ships were withdrawn from service.

above The search for fish from a deep-sea trawler is aided by satellite navigation equipment and a sonar system. Here the sonar display reveals a school of fish near the sea bed.

left Fish from a trawler's net pour into the ship's hold. The largest trawlers are factory ships, in which the catch is cleaned and frozen by the time they have returned to port.

transport

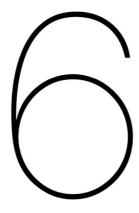

The desire to travel and the need to move heavy loads encouraged man to develop various means of transportation. On land, the first vehicle was the sledge, and a tree trunk or anything else that floated could serve as a crude boat. These primitive means of transport were used many thousands of years ago, but flight did not become possible until the first balloons ascended in the 1700s.

Wheels

It seems likely that the idea of the wheel came about after people had used logs as rollers under heavy loads to make them easier to drag about. Solid wooden wheels had been attached to sledge-like carts in Sumaria by about 3500 BC – soon after the potter's wheel had appeared. About 1,500 years later, spoked wheels were invented, and then came the iron axle, lubricated with fat to make it turn more easily, and the iron rim to make wheels more durable. There was little further development for thousands of years. Dutch inventor Simon Stevin built a two-masted sailing wagon in 1599, but this wind-powered cart needed an almost perfectly flat surface if it was to move at all with normal wind speeds. And so, apart from man, animals were the main source of power for land vehicles until the 1700s and the invention of steam transport.

Steam carriage

The first steam engines powered various kinds of industrial machinery, and many years passed before steam engines were installed in vehicles. The first land vehicle to run under its own power was a three-wheeled steam carriage, constructed in 1769 by French military engineer Nicholas-Joseph Cugnot. It was a cumbersome vehicle, built for hauling heavy guns. Its top speed was a mere 4 kph, and it had to stop several times each hour in order to build up steam. Nevertheless, inventors in several countries started to develop steam-powered vehicles, and a steam bus service started in Paris around 1800. In England, several steam coach services were in operation by the 1830s, typical speeds being 15 to 25 kph.

The disadvantage of steam vehicles was that they had to carry large amounts of fuel and water, and early models took a considerable time to boil the water before a journey could start. Many early steam-powered passenger vehicles were enormous, some having wheels measuring three metres across. A trend for smaller, private vehicles started in Europe and the United States in the 1860s, and steam automobiles continued to be built until the 1920s, by which time speeds of more than 200 kph had occasionally been achieved. However, other means of propulsion had proved to be more suitable for passenger transport, and steam vehicles gradually disappeared from the roads.

Cycling

In ancient times, a bar had sometimes been used to link a pair of cartwheels, one in front of the other, so that a person could sit astride and scoot himself along. The idea reappeared in France in 1791, when the Compte de Sivrae built a machine called the célérifere. In 1817, Karl von Drais invented an improved model with steering, which was called the draisine. Scottish blacksmith Kirkpatrick Macmillan made a machine operated by treadles in 1839 and, in 1861, French coachbuilder Pierre Michaux added cranks and pedals to the front wheel of a draisine. This machine, called the vélocipède, but commonly known in England as the 'boneshaker', was a speedy vehicle, and inspired the production of the 'penny-farthing', or high bicycle, by James Starley in 1870. Peddling the very large front wheel enabled an energetic cyclist to reach dangerous speeds. The forerunner of the cycles common today, with wheels of equal size, and pedals linked by a chain to the rear wheel, was the safety bicycle, invented in 1874 by British engineer H J Lawson. While those with more money invested in motor cars, the bicycle provided the general public with a form of transport that was much cheaper and usually more reliable. Gottlieb Daimler built the first powered cycle in 1885, and the motorcycle industry became firmly established around 1900.

Internal combustion

Steam engines are external combustion engines, the fuel being burnt outside the cylinders where the motive forces are created. The first successful internal combustion engine appeared in the mid-1800s and ran on various fuels, including coal gas, hydrogen and petrol. As with early steam engines, the engines first powered equipment in factories and

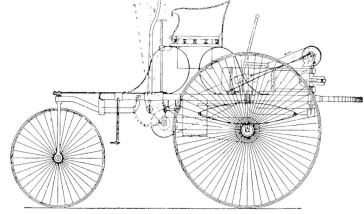

mines. In 1862 Belgian engineer Etienne Lenoir built the first automobile powered by an internal combustion engine. This ran on coal gas and had an average speed of about 4 kph. Many other inventors worked on cars with internal combustion engines at this time, and with varying degrees of success, but it is German engineer Karl Benz who is generally recognized as the inventor of the first practical car to run on a petrol engine. And, as such, he is referred to as one of the fathers of the modern motor car.

The car that led Benz to fame and fortune was an 1885 single-cylinder three-quarter-horsepower two-seater tricycle with an engine at the back. It was two years before Benz managed to find his first customer, but then sales improved as would-be motorists heard about the reliability of his machine. By 1890, he had a factory building four-wheeled cars.

The other influential motor engineer of the time was the German Gottlieb Daimler, who powered a wooden bicycle with an internal

previous Like arteries and veins weaving their way around the body, motorways and roads provide routes for essential services.

far left A chariot used in ancient Assyria, a part of Mesopotamia located at what is now the Iraq-Turkey border area. The first chariots appeared around 3000 BC. Spoked wheels were first used about 1000 years later.

above left Karl Benz, the German engineer whose successful petrol-powered vehicles of the late 1880s led to the development of the modern motor-car industry.

above right The flimsy three-wheeler of 1885 that established Karl Benz as a leading figure in the motor industry. Its single-cylinder petrol engine was rated at less than one horsepower.

combustion engine in 1885. He followed this in 1886 by building his first four-wheeled car.

While the petrol engine was gaining popularity in the 1890s, another German engineer was seeking a more efficient alternative. Whereas petrol engines used sparks to ignite a fuel-air mixture, Rudolf Diesel's approach was to use compression to increase the temperature to ignition point. An attempt to use finely powdered coal dust as engine fuel ended with an explosion in which Diesel nearly lost his life, and he settled instead on using a heavy petroleum oil. Diesel engines are more expensive to produce than petrol engines, as the higher pressures involved require a more sturdy construction, so only a small proportion of cars have been diesel powered. However, diesel vehicles have proved to be the best choice in some cases, notably for urban taxi services and heavy trucks.

In 1908, American manufacturer Henry Ford introduced a car that was to prove extremely popular – the Model T, or 'Tin Lizzie'. The high demand for this vehicle enabled Ford to produce parts by mass production, and to use a moving assembly line. In spite of raising his workers' wages, the savings he made enabled him to sell the car at a moderate price. This strategy was so successful that, by the early 1920s, more than half the vehicles on American roads came from the Ford Motor Company.

Electric vehicles

The first battery-powered cars appeared in the 1880s as a much quieter and cleaner alternative to steam vehicles. These electric cars became popular in the 1900s, but were less powerful than petrol-powered cars. Electric vehicles could not reach high speeds, and the batteries needed frequent charging, making long journeys almost impossible. However, electric cars were excellent for short, slow journeys on congested city streets, and they became popular as delivery trucks. This usage continued even after the general demise of the electric car around 1920, and similar delivery vehicles are widely used today. In recent times, electric cars have been re-introduced as a means of reducing pollution, but batteries with a much greater energy storage capacity are required if the electric motor is ever to replace the petrol engine for general motoring.

Electric trams, running on rails in the streets, were once common in many cities, but many such services were discontinued in the middle of the 20th Century when the streets became crowded with cars. Like trams, trolley buses obtained their power from overhead lines. They were more versatile, not being restricted to running on rails, but many of these services were discontinued too. In the late 1990s, new approaches to solving urban transportation problems resulted in the reappearance of trams in some cities.

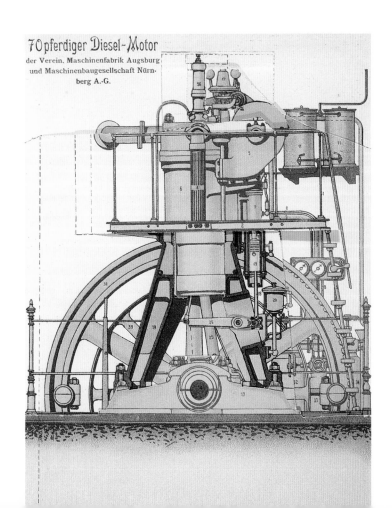

left An early diesel engine. German engineer Rudolph Diesel invented his engine in the 1890s. It proved to be suitable for marine: it was simple and reliable, and its fuel was much safer than petrol and more convenient than the coal used in steam engines.

above Working on the Ford Motor Company assembly line in Detroit, Michigan, in 1909. Using this production technique helped Henry Ford reduce costs and make the Model T, or 'Tin Lizzie', the most popular car in the United States.

right On a modern car assembly line, computer-controlled robots carry out welding and many other operations. The computers are originally 'taught' by a skilled operator, whose movements are recorded electronically.

above French and English forces setting out to repel invaders from Tunisia in 1390. The vessels were merchant ships adapted for war. A forecastle was built on the bow, and the men were armoured for protection in the fierce hand-to-hand fighting that was likely to occur.

Boats and ships

Early boats, such as hollowed logs and frameworks covered with skins, were usually powered by hands or by paddle, although more leisurely journeys could be taken using a river or ocean current to convey the vessel. Thousands of years elapsed before sailors learned to harness the power of the wind. The first sailing boats were probably those used by the Egyptians in the 7th Millennium BC. These were equipped with a single mast carrying a square sail, and oarsmen to assist when the wind dropped. Sailors once confined to the rivers progressed to making sea and ocean voyages in more elaborate vessels. Sail design was slow to advance, and it was not until about 1000 AD that additional, triangular sails were first used. By 1500, elaborate three-masted sailing ships were transporting troops, explorers, passengers and goods.

Steamships

In the mid-1700s, fast ships raced to bring Asian tea and spices to Europe, but a new chapter in seafaring was about to begin with the introduction of steamships. Soon, sailors would have the power to overcome adverse winds and currents.

Steam power was easier to utilise on ships than on road vehicles because a vessel could be made as large as necessary in order to carry the heavy machinery and large fuel supply. Several inventors had attempted to design steam-powered vessels before American engineer John Fitch conducted the first successful trials in 1787. Within just a few years, several primitive steamships came into use on both sides of the Atlantic. Their engines drove various kinds of paddles, some of them like oars, but the paddlewheel proved to be more efficient. Some steamships had one large wheel at the stern, while others has a smaller wheel located on each side.

Going down

While some inventors were working on surface vessels, others were attempting to design underwater craft. The first submarine had been built in 1620 by a Dutchman called Cornelius Drebbel. It was a leather-covered rowing boat, propelled by 12 men, their oars protruding through seals in the skin. Although this strange craft managed to manoeuvre under the River Thames, London, for two hours, the navy did not encourage further development. The first submarine to demonstrate that it might be useful for military purposes was the *Turtle*, a one-man vessel, invented in 1775 by American David Bushnell, and driven by a turning a propeller by hand. The American War of Independence had just started and, the following year, the midget submarine reached an enemy vessel undetected, although it failed in its attempt to attach a mine.

Propellers

By the 1830s, paddle-steamers were widely used for river transport, and some had crossed the Atlantic, although unsuited to the task and not carrying loads. In rough seas, the paddle wheels became inefficient as the rocking repeatedly lifted them out of the water. The problem was

above The first electrically driven submarine, invented by Frenchman C-D Goubet in the mid-1880s. In trials at Cherbourg, the vessel remained submerged for eight hours. Goubet's experiments persuaded the French government to have a 30-tonne submarine built and, around the turn of the century, they had a fleet of ten.

above and above right England's outstanding engineer of the 1800s, Isambard Kingdom Brunel, standing by the anchor chain of the *Great Eastern*, which is shown (above right) dwarfing a frigate moored alongside. Brunel and J Scott Russell designed the *Great Eastern* in the 1850s. When launched in 1858, this vessel was the largest ship ever built, having been designed to carry 3,000 passengers and about 6,000 tonnes of cargo to Columbo, Ceylon (now Sri Lanka) via the Cape of Good Hope. Problems during construction led to worry and overwork for Brunel, and his health suffered so much that he died, aged 53, in 1859, soon after the ship started her maiden voyage.

The *Great Eastern* was the first ship with a double iron hull. It measured 211 metres in length, and had three means of propulsion – a screw propeller, paddlewheels, and sails for six masts. Because of a change of ownership before launch, the *Great Eastern* never sailed to Columbo. Instead, it made journeys across the Atlantic. The ship was also used for cable laying, and established the first successful transatlantic telegraph cable link in the 1860s.

Although the *Great Eastern* was not a financial success, the performance of its many new and experimental features helped designers determine which facilities to provide on future liners.

overcome in 1836, when Swedish engineer John Ericsson patented an efficient screw propeller. A propeller would remain submerged even in the roughest seas, and would also be more efficient than the paddlewheel, which wasted a great deal of energy in disturbing the water. In 1843, British engineer Isambard Kingdom Brunel used the device in his ship *Great Britain,* and this vessel became the first with a propeller to cross the Atlantic. Several earlier ships had used iron in their construction, but the *Great Britain* was the first with a hull made entirely of the metal. The use of iron increased the strength of ships' hulls, enabling more powerful steam engines to be installed and speeds to be increased.

As well as surface ships, submarines adopted the new propeller too. Following various hand-cranked designs, the first self-propelled submarine was launched in France in 1863. Its propeller was turned by a compressed-air machine, thus eliminating the need for a heavy steam engine. Some submarines did use steam power, but a more suitable means of propulsion was the electric motor. The first electrically powered submarine was built in the 1880s by Frenchman Claude-Desiré Goubert.

Turbines

Until the 1890s, surface ships had used piston engines, with cranks to convert the reciprocating action of the pistons into rotary motion. In 1831, American engineer William Avery had invented the practical steam turbine, in which the force of the steam turned blades mounted on a shaft to produce rotary motion directly. British engineer Charles Parsons invented the multistage steam turbine in 1884, a design that proved to be much more reliable and efficient. In 1897, Parsons installed one of his steam turbines on a yacht he was building, enabling it to reach a speed of over 34 knots. Multistage turbines were later used in large ocean going ships and naval vessels.

20th century vessels

The diesel engine, invented in the 1890s, provided an alternative means of propulsion for ships as well as land vehicles. The first diesel engine designed for use on a ship was built in 1911 and fitted to the tanker *Vulcanus*. Diesel engines proved very suitable for marine use, and the oil they ran on was much easier to load and store than the coal used in the furnaces on steamships. Petrol engines were used on some vessels too, but serious accidents occurred when vapour from the fuel was accidentally ignited, and the safer diesel oil is now the generally preferred fuel. Diesel engines also proved to be the most suitable means of powering submarines. Burning diesel fuel when submerged used up too much of the precious oxygen supply, so the engines usually turned generators to charge batteries while on the surface, and these powered the vessels' electric motors when underwater.

Water presents considerable resistance to motion through it by surface vessels and submarines. British inventor Christopher Cockerell found he could avoid this problem and increase efficiency by making a vessel that skimmed over the surface of the water. He had invented the air cushion vehicle, or hovercraft. He patented his design in 1955 and, after a long series of experiments, his first hovercraft SRN1 was launched in 1959. By keeping the craft just above the water, the maximum speed was increased to three times that of a conventional craft of the same size. Hovercraft are now widely used for ferry services and military purposes. One great advantage of the hovercraft is that it can travel over flat ground as well as over water. A typical hovercraft is powered by gas turbine engines that drive fans for lift and propulsion. Steering may be achieved using fins, rudders or air jets.

Another method of lifting a boat hull above the water to increase speed was invented by Italian Enrico Forlanini around 1900, but did not come into general use until the 1950s. Wing-like structures called hydrofoils are attached below the waterline. When the craft moves forward at speed, the hydrofoils produce sufficient lift to raise the main part of the boat clear of the water. Propulsion may be by propeller or water jet.

The most important development in shipping this century occurred in 1954, when the US Navy launched the submarine *Nautilus* – the first nuclear-powered vessel. In 1962, another American ship, *Savannah,* became the first merchant ship to use nuclear power. In such vessels, the heat produced in a nuclear reactor is used to generate steam to turn turbines for propulsion and electricity generation. The advantage of using a nuclear reactor is that it requires very little fuel and no air supply at all. This is particularly important in the case of submarines as it means they can remain underwater for many months, and it can be years before refuelling is necessary.

above Today's modern cruise liners would dwarf Brunel's *Great Britain*. Such massive 'floating hotels' as the *Sovereign of the Sea,* with multiple swimming pools, night clubs and restaurants are powered by efficient, reliable multi-stage turbine engines.

Railways

The first railways were built three centuries before the age of steam. In the early 1500s, wooden railway tracks were used in mines to guide trucks through the narrow passages. Ponies pulled the trucks, or they were arranged to run down a slight incline.

English engineer Richard Trevithick built the first steam locomotive in 1804. In a trial at the Pennydarran Ironworks in Wales, it managed to pull seventy passengers and ten tonnes of steel along cast iron rails. These were too brittle to withstand the weight of the engine and frequently shattered. Unfortunately Trevithick ran out of money and was forced to abandoned his experiments, but others continued experimenting with rail transport.

In 1807, when the Swansea and Mumbles Railway opened in Wales to provide the world's first railway passenger service, horses were used to pull the wagons. For a brief period, the company tried using sails instead, but this experiment was unsuccessful and horses continued in service there until the 1870s. But elsewhere, engineers began to have success with engines. In 1812, Englishman John Blenkinsop designed a commercially successful steam locomotive with a toothed wheel that gripped a rack on the track. Like many other engineers at that time,

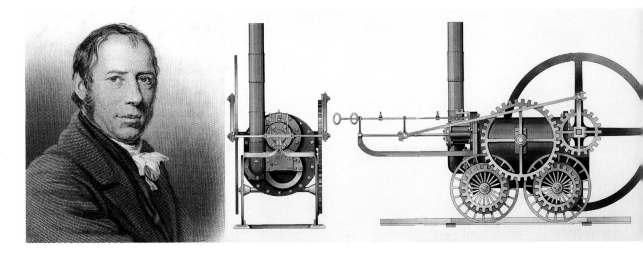

Richard Trevithick (1771-1833)

English inventor and mechanical engineer Richard Trevithick was poorly educated. In spite of his poor academic performance, and difficulties with reading and writing that lasted throughout his lifetime, Trevithick had a great practical ability that enabled him to cope with difficult engineering challenges.

He first worked as an engineer in one of the local tin mines, where steam engines were used for pumping out water. These engines used low-pressure steam for safety, but Trevithick was convinced that he could design a much smaller and more efficient high-pressure steam

engine that would be safe to operate. He completed his first steam engine in 1797, and the design proved highly successful. Besides producing stationary engines for use in the mines, Trevithick also built steam engines to drive road vehicles and, in 1803, built the first railway locomotive (shown above). In 1804, this was demonstrated at the Pennydarran Ironworks, Wales.

Trevithick's locomotives had limited success, because the cast rails tended to shatter, but he went on to build many successful engines for driving farm and industrial machinery. Unfortunately, he was a poor businessman and, in spite of his achievements, he died in poverty.

left The *Mallard* steam locomotive served on the London and North Eastern Railway. On 3 July 1938, the Mallard set a world record for a steam locomotive when it achieved a speed of 203 km/h. That record still stands. The locomotive was designed by the company's chief mechanical engineer, Nigel Gresley.

below The MLU-002 maglev train was first tested at Miyazaki's test centre in Japan in March 1987. This revolutionary type of train is designed to run smoothly at far higher speeds than can be achieved by conventional trains.

Blenkinsop thought this was necessary in order to prevent slipping occurring between metal wheels and metal rails. William Hedley, an engineer from the northeast of England, disproved this theory the following year when his locomotive *Puffing Billy* started hauling heavy coal wagons in the dockyards. Except on steep inclines, there was sufficient friction generated between wheels and rails for hauling even the heaviest of loads.

The northeast of England was also the setting for the first public steam train service, started by the Stockton and Darlington Railway Company in 1825. George Stevenson's *Locomotion No.1* hauled the first trainload of 600 passengers a distance of 34 km. However, this engine proved unreliable in service and Stevenson replaced it in 1829 with a much improved model called *Rocket*. Over 10,000 people turned out to see the new locomotive demonstrate its abilities, and the success of this engine ensured the rapid spread of steam railways throughout Britain and overseas too.

Experiments with electric rail transport started in the 1830s, but the first commercial services did not appear until around 1900. In 1912, trains with experimental diesel engines started trials in Europe, and diesel-electric designs were produced in the following year. Britain's diesel-electric Intercity 125 train is among the fastest in the world, reaching speeds of around 200 km/h. But the fastest trains of all are of a revolutionary design, magnetic forces keeping them levitating just above the track. As they do not touch the track when moving, these maglev trains give an extremely smooth ride, propelled by magnetic forces from linear induction motors. The Central Japan Railway Company's planned Linear Express maglev passenger service is expected to attain speeds of around 500 km/h.

Aviation

If birds could fly, then it was clear to ancient philosophers that it should be possible for man to devise some means of flying too. Through the ages, various ideas were proposed, including attaching wings that flapped, and using evacuated spheres to provide lift, with a sail for propulsion. Hydrogen, discovered in the 1700s, could make a balloon rise, but the materials of the day soon allowed the high-pressure gas to escape. In France, the brothers Joseph-Michel and Jacques-Etienne Montgolfier found an alternative. They had seen burning paper rise from an open fire and decided to use the fumes from a fire to fill a cloth-reinforced paper bag. In September 1783, they managed to use this primitive form of hot-air balloon to carry two birds and a sheep into the air for an eight-minute flight. Man's first flight took place that November in Paris, when Jean Pilâtre de Rozier and the Marquis d'Arlandes ascended in a balloon which was kept up by the hot fumes from a fire that burned wood and straw. After a 25 minute flight, they landed 8 km away at Butte aux Cailles.

By this time, Frenchman Jacques Charles had invented a rubberized silk that would hold hydrogen and, at the beginning of December, Charles and a companion made the first ascent in a hydrogen balloon. Their flight took two hours, and they travelled a distance of 43 km.

Immediately after these historic flights, there were suggestions for making balloons steerable, but it was not until 1852 that the first successful airship appeared. Built by Henri Giffard, another French engineer, this consisted of a cigar-shaped balloon filled with coal gas (mainly hydrogen), with a basket below carrying a coal-fired steam engine that drove a propeller. A large rudder was used for steering.

The person who did most to develop the rigid airship was former German army officer Count Ferdinand von Zeppelin, whose first machine flew in 1900. Its light aluminium alloy framework supported a fabric gas bag containing hydrogen. The Zeppelins, as the count's airships became known, proved extremely reliable, and it was with these aircraft that the world's first airline was started in 1910. After World War I (1914-18), in which the same craft were sent over Britain on bombing raids, airships were developed into luxury passenger craft. Then came a series of disasters. The British *R-101* crashed in 1930, and Germany's *Hindenburg*, the largest airship ever built, caught fire during landing in New Jersey. Nearly 200,000 cubic metres of hydrogen suddenly flared up, and 36 passengers lost their lives. These well publicised disasters shook the public's confidence and, with increasing competition from airplanes, passenger airship services were abandoned.

In recent years, the non-flammable gas helium has become available at a lower price, and airships using this have taken to the skies usually to display advertisements. In the future, airships may become popular for carrying cargo and, perhaps, passengers. Until then, the most common form of lighter-than-air device will continue to be the hot-air balloon, heated by gas jets and used mainly for recreation and advertising.

above The Montgolfier brothers invented the hot-air balloon in 1782. Jean Pilâtre de Rozier and the Marquis d'Arlandes made the first manned flight in 1783.

Gliders

As they still sometimes do today, children in 14th century Europe played with a toy that made a bladed rotor rise into the air when a string was pulled sharply. And, in 15th century Italy, Leonardo da Vinci sketched a form of primitive helicopter and also a machine with wings for a man to flap. But real progress in the development of heavier-than-air machines did not come until the 1800s, when English engineer and scientist George Cayley applied his considerable understanding of aerodynamics to the construction of a glider in 1849. A small boy sat in Cayley's triplane, and a team of men launched it by dragging it down a slope. The flight lasted just a few seconds, and the glider landed safely a short distance away.

The most successful designer of gliders in the 1890s was German engineer Otto Lilienthal, who built several small, lightweight monoplanes and biplanes. Hanging from the structure, he would launch himself from the top of a cliff and soar upwards on currents of rising air, like the pilots of today's hang gliders. Lilienthal died in a crash in 1896.

Since Cayley's demonstration of the glider, engineers had tried to apply power to similar aircraft, using propellers driven by steam engines, but the weight of the machinery made take-off impossible. A solution was in sight with the arrival of the internal combustion engine in the 1870s, for this generated much more power for a given engine weight.

Airplanes

The brothers Wilbur and Orville Wright read about the behaviour of gliders in order to increase their understanding of aerodynamics. They learned how to design gliders having greater stability and ease of control, and they built a lightweight petrol engine for powering an aircraft. On 17 December 1903, the brothers were ready to test their biplane 'flyer' near Kitty Hawk, North Carolina. The first flight that day lasted only a few seconds and covered a distance of just under 37 metres, but that first ever sustained and controlled flight led to the rapid development of the aircraft industry.

below An artist's impression of an early flight by the Wright brothers, covering three miles. On 17 December, 1903, Orville Wright was the pilot on the first, 37 metre flight of the brothers' powered biplane. Of the four flights they made that day near Kitty Hawk, North Carolina, Wilbur's 260 metre hop was the longest.

below right Wilbur and Orville Wright, the American brothers whose brief flights in 1903 showed that powered heavier-than-air machines were capable of taking man into the skies.

Igor Ivanovich Sikorsky (1889-1972)

Although best know for his work on the helicopter in the late 1930s, this Russian-born American aviation pioneer had earlier developed other kinds of aircraft.

He was inspired by the Wright brothers' flights, but found their short duration unimpressive and decided that a vertical take-off machine would be better. He experimented with helicopter design in 1909 and 1910, but failed to make a working machine. From 1910, he concentrated on fixed-wing aircraft and became a highly skilled pilot. In 1913, he designed and flew *Le Grand* – the first four-engined plane.

He moved to the United States in 1919, where he formed the Sikorsky Aero Engineering Corporation in 1923. This became part of the United Aircraft Corporation and produced flying boats for Pan American World Airways. The demand for flying boats declined in the late 1930s, and Sikorsky turned his attentions once again to the helicopter, which other designers had developed in the 1920s and 1930s. Sikorsky had his *VS-300* ready for take-off by September 1939 – less than a year after the project began. The test flight was successful, and an improved version of the helicopter set a record the following year by staying airborne for just over an hour.

below The final version of Igor Sikorsky's *VS-300* helicopter, which was built in 1942. Sikorsky saw the helicopter mainly as a rescue vehicle and passenger carrier, but other engineers later developed it into an effective war machine too.

An entirely new kind of flying machine appeared in 1923, when Spanish engineer Juan de la Cierva invented the autogyro. This had a conventional propeller at the front but, instead of wings, it had a large, unpowered, four-bladed rotor. On take-off, the propeller moved the plane forward, which caused the rotor to start turning. This provided the lift to get the plane off the ground. One advantage of the autogyro was that it could land on a very small site by cutting off the engine and descending almost vertically.

Of much greater importance was the helicopter. Numerous experiments were carried out from 1907, some craft failing to rise more than one metre, and others demonstrating the pilot's lack of control. Etienne Oehmichen was more impressive in 1924, completing a one-kilometre circuit – a record for a helicopter flight at that time. From 1936, the high performance of the German Focke Achgelis Fa-61 finally established the helicopter as a reliable and capable machine. A small vertical rotor on the tail provided stability and prevented the fuselage from turning in the opposite direction to the main rotor. Some later designs had two rotors moving in opposite directions instead.

Towards the end of the decade, engineers and pilots at an airfield were astonished to see an aircraft with no apparent means of propulsion. It had just a pointed nose where they expected a propeller to be, and they could not imagine how it could fly. The first person with the imagination to design a jet aircraft was British engineer Frank Whittle, who patented his engine in 1930. But it was the German Heinkel He-178 which, in 1939, became the first jet plane to fly. By the end of World War II in 1945, the German, British and American forces had all used jets in combat.

In 1966, the British Hawker Siddeley Harrier 'jump-jet' fighter-bomber appeared. Its engines could swivel down for vertical take-off and landing, allowing it to be used in confined spaces.

Jet aircraft were first used for passenger services in the late 1950s. In the 1970s, the giant American Boeing 'jumbo' jets were introduced and, for many people, getting on a plane to travel long distances had become almost a routine procedure, with none of the sense of glamour and adventure that it had held just a few decades earlier.

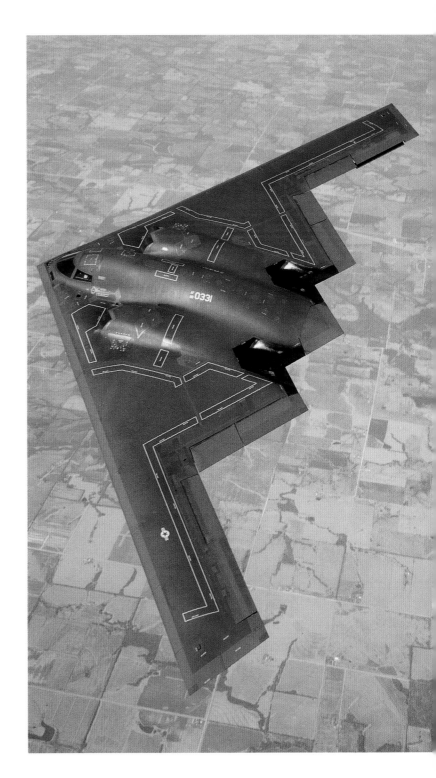

right Stealth planes use modern technology, including shaped surfaces, passive navigation and reducing the heat loss to avoid detection by enemy systems.

7

astronomy and

space exploration

7

Observations of the solar system, and the stars and galaxies far beyond, provide us with clues about the creation of our planet and the universe itself. The first astronomers had only the unaided eye for studying the heavens, so they could distinguish few details and concentrated instead on the star patterns and regular cycles of events that they observed. The stars appeared to be rotating slowly together in fixed relative positions. With a great deal of imagination, the star patterns, or constellations, could be likened to images of gods, heroes, objects and animals. The Sun, Moon and planets appear to travel past a background of 12 of these constellations, known as the zodiac. Because the heavens held such great mysteries, astrologers were able to persuade others that the constellations somehow affected the lives and fortunes of people on Earth, and that future events could be forecast by observing and calculating the positions and movements of heavenly bodies.

The constellations did, however, serve one useful purpose. Nomadic tribes and other travellers came to recognise the patterns and used them for direction finding, for the centre of apparent rotation was above the Earth's North Pole. Settlers, on the other hand, were more interested in the regular movements of the Sun and Moon, which determined the time of day, month and year, and also affected the tides. Astronomy has, therefore, always been of major importance to society.

Early observations

Astronomy sometimes reveals information about our own planet. In the 300s BC, the Greek philosopher Aristotle considered the fact that some stars seen from one country can never be seen from another. He declared that there could be only one reason for this – the Earth could not be flat, as generally believed, but must be a sphere. In about 290 BC, another philosopher, Aristarchus of Samos, suggested that the Sun was at the centre of our planetary system, but it was generally assumed that the

previous The Hubble Space Telescope is an unmanned optical observatory orbiting the Earth at an altitude of about 600 km. It was launched in 1990. Visiting astronauts corrected various defects in 1993, and the telescope has since produced the best astronomical images ever obtained.

left An astronomer in ancient Egypt measuring the relative positions of the stars. It was thought at the time that all the stars were the same distance from the Earth. The Egyptians appear to have used the changing positions of the stars in the sky throughout the year as a calendar

Earth was at the centre of the universe with the other bodies moving around it. The strange thing was that planets were sometimes seen to change their apparent direction of motion across the stellar background. In the 2nd Century AD, the Greek astronomer and mathematician Ptolemy found a possible explanation. He thought that the planets moved in small circles, while also moving in large circles around the Earth. Sometimes, a planet's component of motion resulting from the small orbit would be in the opposite direction to that from the large orbit, and could make it appear that the planet was moving backwards for a while.

Ptolemy's geocentric picture of the universe was accepted for centuries. Others suspected that the Sun was at the centre of our planetary system, but the Church supported the idea that God had created the universe with the Earth at its centre. To suggest otherwise was to deny God's work, and that could invoke a penalty of torture or execution. However, in the 1500s, a Polish doctor called Nicolaus Copernicus was convinced that the Earth and planets orbited the Sun and decided to publish his theories. He completed the final corrections in 1543, as he lay dying, so he had nothing to fear from the Church. His much simpler description of how the planets moved overcame many problems presented by Ptolemy's model and very gradually gained acceptance.

More information was needed about the universe in order to verify the Copernican theory, for some aspects of it presented problems. For example, if the Earth moved around so much, why did the observed star patterns always appear to be the same? The Copernican view was that the patterns of the stars did, in fact, change but that, because they were much farther away than previously believed, the changes were much too small to be seen. New evidence supporting the ideas of Copernicus began to appear early the next century, when the invention of the telescope brought about a surge in astronomical discoveries.

Nicolaus Copernicus (1473-1543)

Copernicus (below left) was a man of many talents, having acquired extensive knowledge of medicine, law, mathematics, theology and astronomy. But he had many doubts about some of the prevailing theories of astronomy, especially with the description of the universe given by Ptolemy in the 2nd Century AD, which placed the Earth at its centre (below right).

From the Earth, other planets sometimes appear to have an irregular motion, and are seen to stop and then reverse their apparent direction of motion. Ptolomy thought this was because, while moving in large circles around the Earth, the planets also moved locally in small circles. This complex model had survived for centuries and did seem to give a reasonable explanation of astronomers' observations. However, Copernicus felt that there must be a simpler answer, and considered the ancient Greek idea that the Sun is at the centre of our planetary system. After years spent calculating the movements of planets, Copernicus was convinced that the heliocentric theory was correct. The Sun was, indeed, at the centre, and all the planets, including the Earth, were in orbit around it.

Refracting telescope

The first optical telescope was made in 1608 by a Dutch spectacle maker called Hans Lippershey. The military were going to find it useful for observing enemy troop movements but, in Italy, Galileo Galilei was told of the device and decided to construct his own for observing the heavens. And so, a year after Lippershey's invention, Galileo became the first astronomer to use a telescope. He made important discoveries: there were mountains on the Moon; Jupiter had at least four moons; the Sun had spots; and, of particular importance, the planet Venus showed a full series of phases, just like our Moon. Galileo found he could explain the Venusian changes only if the sun-centred theory of Copernicus was correct. Sadly, the Church strongly opposed Galileo's theory and eventually forced him to abandon his studies of what they regarded as God's territory.

Bearing in mind that Galileo's telescopes were portable instruments, the largest being only 1.2 metres long, his achievements were remarkable. The lens system in his telescopes magnified by refracting (bending) light. All such instruments are, therefore known as refracting telescopes, or refractors. Like Lippershey, Galileo used a converging objective lens to produce a magnified image, and a diverging eyepiece lens to turn the image up the right way. This design is now generally referred to as a Galilean telescope. Its main disadvantage was that it gave a very narrow field of view. The fact that the image was inverted did not matter because

above left A total eclipse of the Sun occurs when the Moon passes directly between the Sun and the Earth. Such an eclipse enables astronomers to study the Sun's corona — the outer part of its atmosphere.

above A photograph of the Sun, showing sunspots. These cooler, relatively dark areas, typically some 30,000 km across, were first observed by Galileo in the early 1600s.

Galileo Galilei (1564-1642)

The work of Galileo was of such importance that he is sometimes called the father of modern experimental science.

In 1581, he went to the University of Pisa to study medicine, but became more interested in mathematics and general science. He left Pisa in 1585 and, the following year, invented a hydrostatic balance, which measured the density of objects by weighing them in water. His work on finding an object's centre of gravity secured him the position of mathematics lecturer from 1589, back at Pisa University. There he investigated the behaviour of bodies in motion. Galileo became professor of mathematics at the University of Padua in 1592, and stayed there for 18 years. During this period, he completed work describing the acceleration due to gravity, and the trajectories of missiles. He also studied astronomy, and, in 1609, became the first astronomer to use a telescope. Galileo made many important discoveries using this new instrument, and found evidence to support the Copernican theory that the Earth, not the Sun, was at the centre of our planetary system.

Galileo left Padua in 1610, and later published his ideas about the universe. The Church strongly opposed his views, and he spent his last eight years under house arrest.

below Isaac Newton demonstrated that white light is a mixture of colours. This later enabled Chester Moor Hall to correct colour distortion of lenses.

Reflecting telescope

It was Isaac Newton who, in the 1660s, had discovered the cause of chromatic aberration, although he never found a way of correcting it. But, in 1668, he invented the reflecting telescope, which produced very little colour distortion. Instead of an objective lens, this instrument had a concave mirror to gather the light. It reflected the rays onto a small plane mirror, and this, in turn, reflected the rays to an eyepiece lens mounted on the side of the telescope tube. By eliminating the large objective lens responsible for most chromatic aberration in refracting telescopes, Newton obtained almost perfect images, although the eyepiece lens did give rise to a little colour fringing. Other scientists invented different kinds of reflecting telescopes which still bear their names, notably James Gregory of Scotland and N Cassegrain of France.

Achromatic lens

In 1729, an English mathematician called Chester Moor Hall found a way of eliminating the problem of chromatic aberration in lenses. He knew that the human eye contained a lens that did not produce chromatic aberration, and felt sure that a lens with similar properties could be constructed from glass. His solution was to make a compound lens by combining two lenses, one convex and the other concave, consisting of different types of glass – crown glass and flint glass. The combination was designed so that the chromatic aberration introduced by the convex lens was cancelled by the opposite effect introduced by the concave lens. Had the same kind of glass been used for both elements, the magnification produced by the convex lens would have been cancelled out too. But, by using different kinds of glass, the magnifying effect was only partially cancelled, so the combination, called an achromatic lens, produced a magnified image free from colour fringes. Four years later, Moor built the first telescopes incorporating achromatic lenses.

The invention of the achromatic lens meant that relatively short, high-power, high-quality refracting telescopes could be constructed. Large refractors continued to be built throughout the 1800s, but the reflector became the astronomers' preferred instrument in the 1900s. Lenses and mirrors had steadily become larger to improve their light-gathering abilities, and the weight of a heavy lens could make it sag and distort the image formed. Mirrors could be made much lighter and, whereas a lens was supported only around its rim, a mirror could be supported over its entire back surface, thus making it more stable.

there is no right-way-up in space. Later astronomical telescopes had two converging lenses, which formed an inverted image but gave a wider field of view than the Galilean telescope.

Chromatic aberration

One problem with early refracting telescopes was that optical defects caused noticeable distortion, especially at high magnification. Colour distortion, known as chromatic aberration, showed up as colour fringes around the images. This occurred because the glass in a simple lens bends light rays of different colours by different amounts, causing them to come into focus at slightly different distances from the lens. The effect could be reduced by using lenses with relatively little curvature. This gave them a long focal length, so the telescope had to be long, too, in order for the light to be focused. This is why some astronomical telescopes were more than 45 metres long.

above To reduce distortion of colours, some early telescopes had lenses that were slightly curved. This gave them a long focal length (they focused light at some distance from the lens), and so the telescopes had to be long too. Some nineteenth-century telescopes were many tens of feet long.

Modern materials and techniques

One problem affecting both reflectors and refractors is that they may be subjected to large temperature changes, causing expansion or contraction of the optical system and consequent image distortion. A solution came in the 1940s, when the Corning Glass Works, New York, introduced Pyrex glass. When heated, this borosilicate glass expanded only about one-third as much as ordinary glass, so it was an excellent material for making mirrors for large reflecting telescopes. This glass has since been used in several big telescopes, including the world's largest in Zelenchukskaya, Russia – the Special Astrophysical Observatory's 6-metre diameter reflector.

Since the 1840s, images formed by astronomical telescopes have been recorded on photographic plates or film. Stars too faint to be seen can be captured by exposing the light-sensitive material for a prolonged period. During this time, the telescope is turned automatically to follow the apparent motion of the stars, caused by the rotation of the Earth.

A modern optical astronomical telescope may weigh several hundred tonnes, yet it needs a motor less powerful than that in a vacuum cleaner to make it turn on its precision mounting.

A most important discovery came in 1814, when German physicist Joseph von Fraunhofer found that the spectrum of light emitted by a body could reveal the elements present in it. By attaching an instrument called a spectrograph to the telescope, astronomers could now determine the presence of various elements in the stars. In 1842, Austrian physicist Christian Doppler noticed that the coloured lines associated with each element are sometimes displaced towards one end of the spectrum. This occurs because the motion of a body relative to the Earth causes an apparent change in the frequency of the radiated light. A similar effect is noticed when a fast train passes sounding its whistle. The note sounds higher as the train approaches, and lower as it moves away from us. This phenomenon is called the Doppler effect and, in the case of stars, indicates the speed at which they are moving away from us.

In modern observatories, astronomers use spectrographs equipped with extremely sensitive photoelectric devices called CCDs (charge-coupled devices) to detect and analyse the faint light reaching us from the most remote parts of the universe.

Radio telescopes

In 1931, American engineer Karl Jansky, working at the Bell Telephone Laboratories, was trying to find the causes of interference on short-wave radio transmissions. He pointed a highly directional aerial in various directions and listened to the detected signals on a radio receiver. Some interference clearly came from electrical disturbances in the Earth's atmosphere, but there was another, more distant source too. He scanned the sky with the aerial and found a direction in which the interference reached a peak. Jansky had discovered radio waves coming from the centre of our galaxy – the Milky Way.

This was not, as some sensational reports made out, evidence of life somewhere out in space, but the discovery was of great importance and led to the development of radio astronomy. As with light, radio emissions coming from space can be analysed to reveal details about the bodies emitting the radiation. Radio engineer Grote Reber built the first radio telescope at his home in Illinois in the 1930s. It had a dish-shaped aerial nearly 10 metres across. He used his equipment to detect radiation coming from parts of the sky and, in 1944, published his results in the form of a map – the first of its kind. The largest fully steerable radio telescope dish ever built is the 100-metre diameter instrument in Germany. Large single dishes with limited mobility have been constructed, and signals from several conventional dishes may be combined to form a VLA (Very Large Array) with a large effective diameter and greatly improved image resolution in order to pinpoint the sources of radiation. Radio telescopes around the world will eventually be linked to simulate a dish with a diameter equal to that of the Earth. The next step then will be to link a series of widely separated radio telescopes in space.

above The VLA (Very Large Array) radio telescope near Socorro, New Mexico, is the largest of its type. It consists of 27 dishes, each 25 metres across, which can be moved along three railway tracks, each about 21 km long. Signals from the dishes are combined to simulate the performance of a single dish some 27 km in diameter.

Space and beyond

In order to obtain distinct images, optical telescopes need to be situated far from the glare of city lights, at a high altitude to minimize distortion caused by the atmosphere. And radio telescopes need to be as far as possible from sources of man-made electrical interference. Situating telescopes in space therefore has great advantages but, for a thorough investigation of our neighbours in the Solar System, there is no substitute for sending space probes, and man himself, to visit these remote worlds.

Rockets

The key to space travel was an ancient invention formerly used as a weapon. By the 1200s, Chinese soldiers were using gunpowder-charged rockets as weapons, and similar devices appeared later in India, Europe and America. The use of these weapons declined during the 1800s because the rifle was proving more effective on the battlefield. Around the turn of the century, science fiction writers, intrigued by the discoveries of astronomers, were concocting tales of flights through space to the Moon and planets. These stories, in turn, encouraged scientists to work out ways of making such things possible.

Russian theoretical scientist Konstantin Tsiolkovski knew that a spacecraft would have to reach a high speed in order to enter an orbit around the Earth, and an even higher speed would be needed if the craft was to escape from the Earth's gravitational field and travel deep into space. Rocket propulsion needed improving, and a multi-stage system would have to be adopted. A single-stage rocket would need to carry so much fuel that its weight would prevent it from reaching a high enough speed. With a multi-stage rocket, the first, heaviest section, could be jettisoned when its fuel had been used up, and subsequent stages would then take the ever-lighter craft up to the speed required.

American inventor Robert Goddard carried out numerous experiments with rockets from 1908 and came to the same conclusions as Tsiolkovski. In 1919, Goddard published a paper in which he explained the basic principles of space flight. Unfortunately, Goddard's ideas were ridiculed by the press, and he made few public statements about the subject after that, although he did continue experimenting.

One problem was that gunpowder was not an ideal rocket fuel, and Goddard experimented with alternatives. In 1926, he launched the first experimental rocket to use a liquid propellant. It reached an altitude of

left American rocket pioneer Dr Robert Goddard, standing beside one of his rockets in 1926. This was launched on March 16 and became the first successful rocket to use a liquid propellant.

far right NASA's space shuttle *Columbia* on its launch pad before take-off. The shuttle consists of a main orbiter (foreground), a large disposable fuel tank, and two reusable booster rockets.

above Russian cosmonaut Yuri Gagarin in the cabin of *Vostok 1*, in which he became the first person to orbit the Earth. The flight took place on 12 April 1961. Gagarin made one complete orbit and landed safely 108 minutes later. He died in a plane crash in 1968.

left American astronaut Edwin 'Buzz' Aldrin installing a seismograph on the surface of the Moon during the Apollo 11 mission in July 1969. This was the first manned mission to the Moon's surface, Neil Armstrong being the first to set foot on the lunar soil. The third astronaut was Michael Collins.

right An artist's impression of the International Space Station, due to be completed in the early 2000s. The pressurised modules will accommodate six personnel, who will carry out various scientific experiments.

just 56 metres before crashing to the ground, but later designs were more successful and Goddard's achievements in this field were to earn him recognition as the father of rocket science.

In Germany, Hermann Oberth played an important role in developing rocket science in the 1920s, and it was a book by Oberth on space rockets that inspired 13-year-old Wernher von Braun to study rockets. Von Braun eventually assisted Oberth in his work and later became technical director of Germany's military rocket development team. They made great advances in the 1930s and throughout the war (1939-45) with the development of highly efficient solid propellants and the V-2 long-range liquid-propelled rocket missile.

After the war, von Braun and many other German scientists went to work on rockets in the United States. During the time of the 'cold war' between the USSR and the United States, both countries developed long-range rocket weapons, and this work led to the production of rockets capable of launching satellites into orbit around the Earth. In the 1950s, scientists in the East and West found themselves involved in the 'space race' – the quest to get spacecraft into orbit around the Earth, and to the Moon and beyond. All this eventually became possible because of advances, not just in rocket science, but in computer technology too. For so many calculations have to be carried out rapidly during a space mission that only computers can handle the task.

Space age

In 1957, the successful launch of the artificial satellite *Sputnik 1* by the USSR marked the start of the space age. And it was an army team led by von Braun that, in 1958, launched America's first satellite, *Explorer 1*. Following Soviet and American successes in getting men into Earth orbit and back safely to Earth, and in sending unmanned probes to the Moon, 1969 saw American astronauts Neil Armstrong and Edwin Aldrin become the first people to set foot on the Moon. Since then, much of the effort in space exploration has been aimed at sending unmanned probes to other planets in the Solar System. In 1975, modules from two American *Viking* space probes landed on Mars, photographed the surface and tested the soil to see if life ever existed on that planet. The tests were inconclusive, and so the mystery remains.

The most successful unmanned mission started in 1977, when the American spacecraft *Voyagers 1* and *2* were launched on an epic journey that took them first to Jupiter, then on to other planets where many important discoveries were made. For example, pictures sent back from *Voyager 2* revealed that Uranus, previously thought to have five moons, actually has a total of 15.

Scientists now have the Space Shuttle to ferry them to and from space, where they may stay for months to carry out experiments in an orbiting laboratory. From Earth, astronomers can use the orbiting Hubble Space Telescope to get a clear view of the heavens. And the first major project of the 21st Century will be the completion of the Freedom Space Station. Some years later, perhaps in the 2020s, a permanent base on Mars will be established to provide an opportunity for exploring an entirely new world and, perhaps, for populating it too.

measurements

8

The 'three dimensions' are usually taken to mean length, breadth and width, and time may be regarded as the fourth. But, in the field of scientific measurement, the three basic dimensions are length, mass and time, and most other kinds of measurement can be expressed in terms of these three quantities. Length, mass and time are also the quantities that have been of fundamental importance to the development of mankind.

Length

Methods of measurement became a necessity as soon as primitive man developed a sense of ownership. Counting answered the question of 'how many' with precision, but other methods of assessing quantity were less accurate. Using practical units to measure distance and size created problems as, with no agreed standards, lengths were based on such things as paces and parts of the body. The cubit, for example, was based on the distance from the elbow to the fingertips – about half a metre – but its size varied from person to person. This was not good enough for the ancient Egyptians, who needed a more accurate system of measurement for calculations involving building and land surveying. So they introduced a standard known as the royal cubit, about 524mm, which was marked by lines in a slab of granite. Accurate substandard rulers were copied from this, and distributed so that they could be copied to make practical rulers. The cubit was divided into 7 palms of nearly 75mm, based on the distance across the middle joints of the four fingers, and the palm was divided into four digits of around 19mm – about the width of a finger. For workers requiring greater accuracy, the digits were subdivided too, the smallest divisions being sixteenths of a digit.

With an established system for measuring length, people could carry out accurate land surveys, calculate areas, and make containers of known volume to measure liquids, powders and grain.

In spite of this great advance made so long ago, little was done to establish international standards of length. Even in the 1300s, there were still variations between the measures adopted by different towns within the same country. So 100 feet of rope bought in one town might be regarded as less than 90 feet elsewhere. This situation could not be allowed to continue and, in England, Edward I established the first standard for the yard in 1305. It consisted of an iron bar, with lines marking the yard, subdivided into feet and inches.

The metre was introduced in France in the 1780s as part of a new decimal system of weights and measures. A committee specified that the new length standard was to be one ten-millionth of the length of a line passing through Paris and joining the Equator to the North Pole. Determining the length of this line presented great difficulties and took surveyors several years. The standard metre was then marked on a bar of platinum, chosen for its resistance to corrosion. This platinum metre became the standard in 1793. By the 1960s, many other countries had redefined their yard as 0.9144 metre, so they no longer had to maintain length standards themselves.

previous close-up of a sundial showing the shadow cast onto the dial indicating the hours of the day.

above A ship's navigator using a sextant to measure the angle of the Sun above the horizon. From this, and the time at which the measurement is taken, the ship's latitude can be found.

The need for accurate measurement of distance has led to the invention of many specialized instruments. In 1631, the French mathematician Pierre Vernier invented the Vernier calliper, which is still widely used by engineers for measuring small distances. With a ruler, there is a limit to how close the graduations can be before they become unreadable, and this limits the accuracy attainable. The Vernier calliper has a pair of jaws that are adjusted so that they just touch the object being measured. A modified sliding measuring scale moves against a standard fixed scale, and alignment of lines on the two scales gives an easily read reading of high accuracy.

Extremely small distances can be measured by using an ordinary microscope to view the object against a finely engraved scale. A travelling microscope is specially designed for measurement. Turning a knob moves the instrument over the object being measured and, when a mark super-imposed on the view has moved from one side of the object to the other, the corresponding distance is read from a scale.

It is sometimes more convenient, and often essential, to measure distances indirectly. Some other quantity is measured and the distance obtained by calculation or from a calibrated scale. Radar, for example, indicates the range of distant objects by measuring the time it takes for radio signals to bounce back from them. As the speed of the signals is known, the elapsed time can be used to obtain a distance reading and display. An aircraft's radio altimeter uses radar in a similar way to measure the plane's height above the ground. The pressure altimeter works like an aneroid barometer, invented in the mid-1800s by Lucien Vidie, and uses the fact that air pressure decreases with altitude to work out height. This instrument contains a thin vacuum capsule, the walls of which are forced in by an amount determined by the external air pressure. Changes in air pressure cause the sides of the capsule to move in or out, and the movement is magnified by levers and gears so that it can give a reading on a meter, calibrated to show height. The pilot has to set the ground-level air pressure, which is obtained by reports from weather stations. The altimeter then shows the aircraft's height above the ground.

The decrease in air pressure with height also lowers the boiling point of liquids. Before more accurate methods became available, explorers sometimes measured the temperature at which water boiled so that they could work out the height of the land. An ordinary mercury or alcohol thermometer happens to use the opposite effect, the height of the column of liquid giving an indication of temperature. Such a thermometer, and any other instrument that uses variations in one quantity to represent variations in another quantity, is described as an analogue device.

Mass

For most general purposes, mass and weight amount to the same thing and can be expressed in the same units, although they are actually quite different scientifically.

The mass of an object is a measure of the amount of matter it contains, whereas an object's weight is a force that depends on other factors too. For example, an astronaut's weight is greatly increased by a rocket's

left A portable air barometer, containing air, spirit and mercury, and dating from the mid-1800s. Ordinary mercury barometers were too cumbersome to carry about, being about a metre long. Modern portable barometers are of the aneroid type, containing an evacuated metal capsule that expands or contracts according to the air pressure.

acceleration during launch, but becomes zero during a space walk. The astronaut's mass, however, remains unaltered.

No such considerations bothered early civilizations, and weighing was introduced as a convenient method of assessing quantities of goods. The first weighing instrument was the equal-arm balance, which appeared around 5000 BC. Scale pans were hung from the ends of a rod, and this was suspended by a cord or chain attached to its midpoint, so that an object placed in one pan could be balanced by weights on the other side. Numerous systems of weights were devised by ancient civilizations and, as with lengths, standards and substandards were eventually established to ensure uniformity among the measures in general use.

The equal-arm balance is still used in some markets to this day, and the mechanical chemical balance is a high-precision laboratory instrument based on the same simple principle. The spring balance is an example of a weighing instrument that use no weights. When an object is placed in the pan, it stretches a spring, and a pointer moves down a calibrated scale to indicate the weight. The reading given by this kind of instrument depends on the local force of gravity and indicates true weight. On the Moon, the spring balance would show an object's weight to be much lower than that measured on the Earth because the Moon's gravitational attraction for the object would be lower. By contrast, the equal-arm balance would give the same result in both cases because gravity acts equally on both pans. The equal-arm balance therefore measures an object's mass, rather than its weight.

below The Dutch scientist and mathematician Christiaan Huygens built the first successful pendulum-regulated clock in 1656. Here, Huygens is shown presenting his pendulum clock to King Louis XIV of France.

Time

The Earth's movement around the Sun determines the length of the year and, because the Earth's axis is tilted, this movement causes seasonal changes too. The Earth also regulates daily routines, its spin bringing the dawn and sunset.

Problems arose when people settled and started using a calendar to plan their work in the fields. The Earth completes about 365 spins in the time it takes to orbit the Sun, so a calendar with the same number of days in each year gradually gets out of step with the seasons. The Roman calendar was originally linked to phases of the Moon, and this led to discrepancies too. As a result, Julius Caesar introduced a new calendar, following advice from Egyptian astronomer Sosigenes. To correct previous errors, the year 46 BC had extra days added to make a total of 445 days. Then, from 45 BC, there were 365 days per year for three years, followed by a leap year of 366 days, making the average length of a calendar year exactly 365 days. This was close, but the true length of a solar year was more than 11 minutes shorter, and gradually the calendar was found to be getting out of step with the seasons again.

Pope Gregory XIII made a 10-day correction in 1582 by declaring that the day after October 4 would be October 15. This made him unpopular with some people, who thought he had somehow robbed them of a part of their lives. Besides correcting the date, Gregory also specified that century years would not be leap years unless they were multiples of 400. This ensured that the calendar would keep in step with the solar year to an accuracy of better than two hours per millennium, and the Gregorian calendar is the one widely used today.

The first device for showing the time of day was a form of sundial called a gnomon. This appeared around 3500 BC, and indicated the time by the length of a shadow cast by a stick. In about 300 BC, the Babylonians started using sundials in which the time of day was judged by the position of the shadow on an arc, which was divided into 12 hours.

The desire to know the time at night led to various inventions, an early example being the ancient Babylonian clepsydra. In one simple type, water was allowed to leak from a vessel, and the level of the remaining water indicated elapsed time. The sand-glass worked on a similar principle, but used the trickle of fine sand from one section of a sealed container to another. Candles were widely used for timekeeping, notches in the side giving a rough indication of the time they had been burning.

John Harrison (1693–1776)

English mechanic and inventor John Harrison (above) started constructing his first high-accuracy clock in 1728. In 1714, the British government had offered £20,000 for a timepiece that would allow a navigator to calculate longitude to within half a degree after a voyage to the West Indies, and the prize was still unclaimed. Ordinary clocks could not cope with the motion of a ship in the heavy seas and extremes of temperature met on long journeys. Errors in navigation, caused by timing inaccuracies, had resulted in many maritime disasters.

Harrison completed his first large chronometer in 1735, and this was accurate enough to meet the high standard required. However, Harrison saw ways of improving accuracy, and built more chronometers, each smaller than the one before.

In 1762, he finished his Number 4 marine chronometer (right), which was small enough to fit the palm of the hand, and was the most accurate of all. On arrival in the West Indies, this timepiece showed an error of only five seconds. Although all his chronometers had met the standard, he was not paid in full until 1773.

Public clocks with completely mechanical mechanisms were produced in Europe from the early 1300s. A heavy weight, with a rope attached, pulled the mechanism around, and some of the early ones struck a bell once on the hour. Later that century, clocks were provided with an hour hand to give a continuous indication of time, and smaller versions were made for use in the home. A minute hand would have been pointless, because clocks were so inaccurate in those days.

A rocking mechanism called a foliot regulated early mechanical clocks, but these were poor timekeepers. Then, in the early 1580s, Italian physicist Galileo Galilei discovered that, for small swings, the timing of the to-and-from movements of a pendulum was remarkably regular. It was not until 1641 that Galileo designed a clock regulated by a pendulum, but he died before building it, and the task was left for others.

Astronomers needed a more accurate form of timekeeping for their work and, in 1656, Dutch astronomer Christiaan Huygens made the first successful pendulum-regulated clock. Errors were reduced from several minutes per day to just a few seconds and, from the 1670s, clocks were provided with minute hands.

In 1658, the English scientist Robert Hooke invented a regulator in the form of a spring, which controlled a balance wheel that turned back and forth. Huygens was probably the first to make the spring into a spiral hairspring, which continually coiled and uncoiled as the balance wheel oscillated. Unlike other forms of regulator, the balance wheel kept good time even when it was moved about. This made it particularly suitable for use in watches which, up to that time, had been notoriously inaccurate.

Astronomers were not the only people to need accurate timing for recording their observations of the heavens. Ships' navigators needed an accurate form of clock in order to work out longitude when using a sextant, and timekeeping inaccuracies caused several errors in navigation that resulted in disaster. In 1762, English inventor John Harrison won the prize of £20,000 offered by the British government for making a timekeeper that allowed longitude to be calculated to within half a degree following a voyage to the West Indies. He obtained great accuracy by devising a technique to virtually eliminate the inaccuracies normally caused by temperature changes.

In more recent times, new methods of accurate timekeeping have been devised. Low-cost mechanisms, regulated by a vibrating quartz crystal, give an accuracy to rival Harrison's chronometers. And atomic clocks, regulated by the vibrations of caesium atoms, can be accurate to a small fraction of a second in a thousand years.

Measurements today

Current units of measurement still differ from trade to trade, and country to country, but the international scientific community has settled on the Système International d'Unités, which is known as SI. This was based on the metric system and adopted in 1960. The SI units of length, mass and time are the metre, kilogram and second. The metre is now defined as the distance travelled by light in a specified fraction of a second; the kilogram is defined by a prototype consisting of a platinum-iridium cylinder; and the second is defined as the time taken for caesium-133 atoms to emit a certain number of waves of radiation under specified conditions.

Early travellers had the Sun and stars as aids to direction finding. The magnetic compass, probably first used by the Chinese nearly 1,000 years ago, was more convenient as it required little expertise, but could give misleading results as the Earth's magnetic field is extremely irregular in some places. The Arabic compass shown above left dates from the 9th or 10th Century.

To determine position, especially at sea, latitude and longitude can be found by using a sextant to measure the angle of the Sun or a star at a particular time, and referring to navigation tables. But today's navigators no longer need this traditional skill. Instead, they can use a technique called GPS – Global Positioning System.

Twenty-one Navstar satellites orbit the Earth, each transmitting a radio signal giving its identity and position, together with the time obtained from an on-board atomic clock. From the differences in timing of the signals coming from different satellites, a hand-held receiver (above right) can calculate its own position with extreme accuracy.
The model shown here can determine its position anywhere in the world to within 100 metres, and receivers used by the military, surveyors and in vehicle guidance systems are even more accurate.

9 writing and printing

The origins of writing are uncertain, although there is evidence that sets of small clay shapes found in Mesopotamia, and dating back to 8000 BC, may have been used as tokens to represent names, objects and numbers. Similar shapes are found in the inscriptions on Sumarian clay tablets made around 3000 BC. Later, some extra symbols were introduced to represent common sounds.

The earliest examples of Chinese writing date from the 2nd Millennium BC. By then, the system had already evolved into an elaborate scheme with more than 2,500 characters. Many were simple pictures representing objects, but some things were hard to depict this way, so an object with a similar name was shown instead. Confusion could arise in cases where several words sounded similar, so extra strokes were added to some pictures to indicate which of several meanings was intended. To this day, the meaning of Chinese writing is clearer to a reader, but more difficult for a listener unless aided by gesticulations for distinguishing between alternative meanings. Many other forms of writing, such as English, evolved to represent the sounds of the spoken language.

Materials and implements

The great variety of materials used for writing on in ancient times include clay and wax tablets, slabs of wood and bone, sheets of cloth and metal, and pieces of vellum (calf's skin) and parchment (sheep or goat's skin). By the middle of the 4th Millennium BC, the Egyptians had devised a method of making smooth sheets of writing material from reeds. This papyrus became widely used, and fragments of ancient documents recorded on this material have survived to this day in the dry desert sands. Paper may have been used first in ancient China in the 1st Century AD, but many other writing materials were available, and the use of paper took centuries to spread to the West.

Writing implements varied according to the material being written on, and affected the style of the writing produced. In ancient times, a simple stylus, usually made of wood, bone or metal, was used to inscribe characters in clay or wax, and a reed or brush could be used to apply ink to other materials. The Greeks and Romans used reeds and metal pens, and the quill became popular in some parts of Europe. Various animal and vegetable materials were extracted and made into ink. One method of preparing black ink was to mix gum from a tree with fine soot particles obtained as lampblack.

Before the modern pencil was invented, solid markers used for writing included lead rods. In the late 1500s, pieces of almost pure graphite glued into wooden holders were found to be more suitable for writing, although graphite was then thought to be just another form of lead. In 1795, French chemist Jaques Conte found he could determine the hardness of pencil 'lead' by forming it from powdered graphite and fine clay, mixed in various proportions. In the mid-1800s, American inventor William Monroe devised the first pencil making machine. The propelling pencil was invented in 1879 by the Eagle Pencil Company.

The late 1800s also saw the introduction of the fountain pen, which contained a small reservoir of ink to save the writer from having to keep

previous Hieroglyphics, inscribed on the temple of King Thutmosis III at Samnawest, Egypt. Hieroglyphics were used mainly for religious inscriptions: the word comes from the Greek for 'sacred carving'.

below The first known illustration of papermaking, from 1568. A waterwheel drives the pulping machine (left) and the press to its right. The worker is spreading pulp onto a frame, prior to pressing.

dipping the nib in an inkwell. The first successful fountain pen, the invention of American L E Waterman, appeared in 1884.

Ball-point pens with ink reservoirs first appeared in the 1890s, but it was not until the 1930s that a successful design was produced. This was the invention of Hungarian Lazlo Biro, and pens of this type are widely known as 'biros' to this day. More modern designs with internal reservoirs include felt-tip pens and types with harder tips made from porous plastic.

Printing

The Chinese may have invented a form of printing in the 2nd Century AD, soon after they started using writing paper. The technique may have arisen from the custom adopted by pilgrims of transferring images of religious carvings onto sheets of paper.

Wood-block printing was another invention of the Chinese. By the 600s, they were carving the text for complete pages of a book on blocks of wood, which were then coated with ink and used for printing. This laborious process was used for material required in large quantities, but it was much quicker to copy documents by hand when just a few duplicates were needed. The Chinese also devised other printing methods, including the use of movable type, but thousands of different characters were needed for the Chinese language, and this made the printing system so complicated that it did not become widely used at that time.

right A page from the first Bible of Johannes Gutenberg, published in the 1440s, shows that he had mastered the process of using movable type for printing. It was the first book produced in this way. The Gutenberg Bible is also known as the 42-line Bible, as it has 42 lines to the column.

left An artist's impression of Johannes Gutenberg producing a religious text on his letter press in the mid-15th Century. The individual letters were held in wooden blocks with small metal spacers between them.

Metallographic printing

Most books continued to be copied by hand until the 1400s, when various printing techniques were developed in Europe. Some wood-block printing was carried out, but craftsmen realised that it should be possible to do away with carving and reproduce letters of the alphabet repeatedly using metal dies. The result was a technique known as metallographic printing, probably first used in Holland around 1430. Bronze or brass dies were used to punch the text, letter by letter, into a sheet of soft metal or a clay tablet. When a page had been completed, molten lead was poured over it to produce a cast that could be used for printing.

Letterpress

The metallographic process soon reached Germany, where it was studied by silversmith Johann Gutenberg. For text, the technique was far superior to wood-block printing, but punching the characters one-by-one produced uneven lines of text. Gutenberg was sure he could devise a better system and, by 1450, had developed a technique for commercial printing using movable metal type.

Dies carved in metal were used to make several metal castings of each character. These were stored systematically in open cases for use by the printer. To set a line of text in type, the required characters were selected and inserted into a wooden holder. Lead blanks were used as necessary to adjust the spacing. The lines of type were then assembled in a frame, inked and pressed onto paper to produce prints. This process became known as letterpress, and enabled Gutenberg to produce printed books of high quality. Most notable of these was the Gutenberg Bible of 1455.

Letterpress printing became widely adopted, small print runs being produced direct from the assembled type. To avoid wearing out the expensive dies on long print runs, a mould was produced from the type and used to cast a metal printing plate.

Lithography

Little changed in the printing trade for more than 300 years. Then, in 1796, German writer Alois Senefelder developed a simple and cheap method of printing. It was based on the fact that grease and water do not adhere. He used a greasy crayon to draw a design on a stone slab, which he then dampened with a weak solution of gum. The gum soaked into the stone. He then applied a greasy ink, and this stuck to the crayon design, but not to the damp, unmarked parts of the stone. The design was finally transferred to a sheet of paper by pressing it on the stone. The technique was called lithography. Senefelder later found that a sheet of zinc could be used instead of stone, and this was much easier to handle. The first lithographic printing machines appeared in the 1850s. Highly skilled printers used the litho process to produce coloured art prints of the highest quality. Sometimes as many as 20 specially selected coloured inks were applied in order to achieve the desired effect.

Gravure

Traditional etchings and engravings had been made for centuries by applying ink to lines, eaten away by acid or cut in the surface of a metal plate. This technique was known as gravure printing. With the arrival of photography in the 1800s, a method was needed to reproduce the pictures in print. From the 1860s, light-sensitive coatings were applied to

Typewriter

A Fitch typewriter of the mid-1880s . The typewriter was the invention of Christopher Sholes, former editor of an American newspaper and once apprenticed to a printer. In 1864, Sholes and Samuel Soulé invented a machine for numbering pages automatically. A friend called Carlos Glidden suggested that they might be able to make a machine that would print text as well as numbers – an idea already being considered by other inventors. Success came in 1868, when the three men were granted a patent for their invention. The Remington Arms Company purchased the rights to the machine in 1873, and the machine eventually became the most widely used of all business machines. The first typewriters were purely mechanical, but electric models followed and, in more recent years, electronic typewriters and more elaborate dedicated word processing machines. Today, desktop computers with a wordprocessing program have largely taken over the role held for so long by the typewriter.

metal printing plates so that images could be transferred to them photographically, and chemical processes were used to etch the images into the plates. In the photograveur process, developed in the 1880s by Czech inventor Karl Klic, the image was split up into thousands of tiny cells of equal area, but differing in depth. The deep areas held most ink and printed as black, whereas shallower cells reproduced in shades of grey. In most processes, the cells are of equal depths but differ in area. So all the printed dots that make up the image have the same density but, when viewed from a distance, the varying dot size gives the illusion that various shades are present.

Hot metal machines

While techniques for reproducing pictures were being developed, other inventors were trying to find ways of speeding up the typesetting process.

In 1884, German-born American inventor Ottmar Mergenthaler invented the Linotype machine, which automatically cast lines of type from hot metal according to keys pressed by an operator. This greatly speeded the time taken to get words into print and also reduced costs.

In 1885, Tolbert Lanston invented another kind of hot-metal machine called the Monotype. This cast individual letters and was more suitable for work involving complex layouts rather than solid columns of text.

Printing today

Traditional techniques are still used by many printers, but most large-scale printing today depends on a combination of computer technology, photographic processes and lithography. A magazine journalist may type a story on a desktop computer and then transfer the file electronically to other staff for editing and layout. Conventional photographs can be scanned to convert them to electronic form for display on a layout screen together with the text. Alternatively, images may be obtained in electronic form directly from a digital camera. A whole magazine may be put together on screen and computer files transmitted by wire to the printer.

Assuming that the publication is to be reproduced in colour, four sheets of film are normally produced for each page, showing the cyan, magenta, yellow and black content of the images. Splitting full-colour images into these components is called colour separation. The images on the film are used in a photographic process to produce printing plates, one for each of the four colours used in printing.

A typical high-speed colour printing press is an offset litho machine. Offsetting means that the plates do not print directly onto the paper. Instead, the ink is transferred to a rubber-coated roller, which presses against the paper. The flexibility of the rubber ensures that a clear print is made, even on rough paper and on other materials, such as metal and plastic. Web offset machines use a continuous roll of paper called the web, rather than individual sheets, and rollers can print on both sides of the paper at the same time.

Although only four colours are normally used in the printing process, the final images appear to be in full colour. The photographs in this book have been reproduced by the four-colour process, and close inspection under a magnifying glass will reveal patches of the four printing colours used and the structure of the dot patterns that gives the illusion of variable colour density.

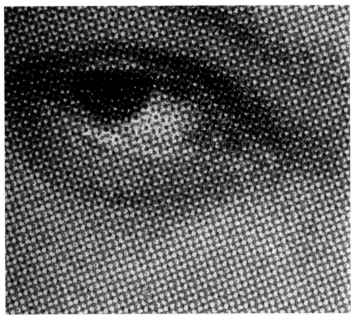

top A technician inspecting the quality of a set of pages printed using the four-colour process.

above A close-up of an image printed by the four-colour process. The four colours used are cyan (blue-green), magenta (red-purple), yellow and black. Various combinations of these colours are used at various intensities to give the illusion of a full-colour picture.

10

photography and the cinema

10

Nicéphore Niepce (1765-1833)

French inventor Nicéphore Niepce (top) made the first permanent photographic image from nature in 1826. He became interested in photographic reproduction techniques when experimenting with lithographic printing in 1813. At first, his artistic son assisted by copying drawings onto a lithographic stone. When the son entered military service, Niepce, being unskilled at drawing, started looking for a way of transferring engravings onto a hard surface automatically. He succeeded in 1822, by placing a transparent picture on a plate coated with a form of asphalt, and leaving them in the sunlight for several hours. The resulting images became known as heliographs, or sun drawings (example above). Besides copying engraved images by contact, Niepce also tried using a sensitized plate to capture the image formed by a camera obscura. Earlier experiments had failed because he had been unable to make the image permanent, but he succeeded with a bitumen-coated pewter plate in 1826. After an exposure of eight hours, followed by chemical development, he had made the first permanent photograph, which showed the view through a window.

Although photography is a fairly recent invention, a form of camera was known to the ancient Greeks around 300 BC. Camera obscura is Latin for 'dark chamber', and referred to a room into which light could enter only through a small hole near the middle of one wall. The rays passing through the hole fell onto a screen on the opposite wall and formed an inverted image of the scene outside. Besides being an interesting novelty, the camera obscura had practical uses too. It enabled astronomers inside the room to watch a solar eclipse without harming their eyes, and artists could study the way light 'drew' images of three-dimensional objects on a flat surface.

In the 1500s, some artists used a small model of the camera obscura as a drawing aid. In one type, a mirror reflected an upright image onto the paper or canvas for the artist to trace. The main problem with the early camera obscura was that the image it formed was quite dim. The brightness could be increased by enlarging the hole to let in more light, but this blurred the picture, as each incoming ray fell on a greater area. In 1568, Italian scientist Giovanni Battista della Porta used a converging lens to focus the light rays. This arrangement produced an image that was both bright and sharp.

Drawing by light

'Photography' means 'drawing by light', and resulted from the discovery of light-sensitive chemicals that could automatically record the image formed in a camera. In the 1500s, alchemists were aware that some silver compounds darkened soon after forming. German scientist Johann Schulze studied the phenomenon in the 1720s, demonstrated that the effect was caused by exposure to light, and produced patterns by allowing sunlight to fall on paper coated with a silver salt. It could be argued that these images, which included silhouettes of letters and words, were the first photographs, as they had been formed by light, but they had no practical uses as the material quickly darkened all over when further exposed to light for viewing. The next requirement was a method of making such images permanent.

In the early 1800s, French inventor Nicéphore Niepce was trying to find a way of using light to copy engravings onto a hard surface. He took an engraving and made the paper transparent by soaking it in oil. Then he placed the paper on a metal plate coated with a solution of black, light-sensitive asphalt. After exposure to sunlight for several hours, most of the asphalt had hardened, but the parts under the lines of the engraving had been shielded from the light and were still soft. On soaking the plate in lavender oil, the dark, hardened part of the coating remained, but the unaltered parts representing the image dissolved away, exposing the bright metal surface below. In this way, a clear and permanent negative image of the engraving was formed.

The first photographs

Niepce continued his experiments throughout the 1820s, and transferred images onto stone, glass, silver, zinc and pewter. And it was with a sensitized pewter plate that, in 1826, he took the first photograph from

previous A cinema projection box. Today's projectors use a xenon projection lamp, instead of the carbon arc type, which needed frequent adjustment, so one operator can now cope with the equipment in several auditoriums.

above In this large camera obscura, light from outside passes into the chamber through a hole in the wall, and is reflected by a mirror. The light then passes through a lens, which forms an image on the screen.

nature. For this, he put the plate in the back of a small camera obscura, pointed it through a window, and left it there all day. The resulting image, showing the courtyard of his house, is now kept in a collection at the University of Texas.

Niepce came to photography through his interest in printing, and his desire to transfer images onto stone for reproduction by lithography. Few of his images printed successfully, and he died in 1833 before perfecting the process. Fortunately, at the end of 1829, a scenery painter called Louis Daguerre had formed a partnership with Niepce, and he continued the work on light-sensitive materials after Niepce died.

In the early 1830s, the need for extremely long exposure times meant that it was virtually impossible to take photographs of people or anything else that moved. Then, in 1835, Daguerre devised a process that cut typical exposure time to under 30 minutes. He used a silvered copper plate, sensitized with iodine, and the image was made visible by exposing the plate to mercury vapour. The first photographs produced in this way were not permanent, as the silver iodide remaining in the lighter parts of the images slowly darkened on exposure to light. However, in 1837, Daguerre found that he could remove all traces of the iodide by treating the plates with a solution of sodium chloride (common salt), 'fixing' the image. This system of photography became known as the daguerreotype process. It was sold to the French government in 1839, after which it became widely used and renowned for the clarity of its images.

Talbot's negatives

English scientist William Fox Talbot had not heard about the developments in France when, in 1835, he found a way of using light-sensitive chemicals to record the images formed by his camera obscura. An important feature of his system was the use of sensitized paper instead of metal plates. The chemical he used was silver chloride, which formed particles of metallic silver on exposure to light. These particles were so fine that an optical effect made them appear black. Fox Talbot soaked the paper in sodium chloride solution to fix the image. When the paper was dry, it showed a negative image, but he could obtain a positive print by passing light through it and onto another sheet of the paper. The best-known of his early photographs is one he took of a window at his Wiltshire home, Lacock Abbey. Fox Talbot found that his early pictures were not permanent, and sought a more effective fixing solution. He perfected his system in 1839, when he replaced the sodium chloride with sodium hyposulphite – still commonly known as photographers 'hypo'.

Fox Talbot's negative-positive system was extremely important because it meant that any number of prints, which he called photogenic drawings, could be obtained from a negative. The exposure time was originally an hour or more, but he further improved the system in 1840, using gallic acid to develop the image after an exposure of only a minute. This new system also produced clearer prints, which he called calotypes or talbotypes. Fox Talbot's later work included the invention of a system for transferring photographic images to the printing press.

below The earliest photographic negative in existence, which shows a latticed window. William Fox Talbot, the inventor of the negative-positive process, took the picture in 1835 at his home in Lacock Abbey, Wiltshire.

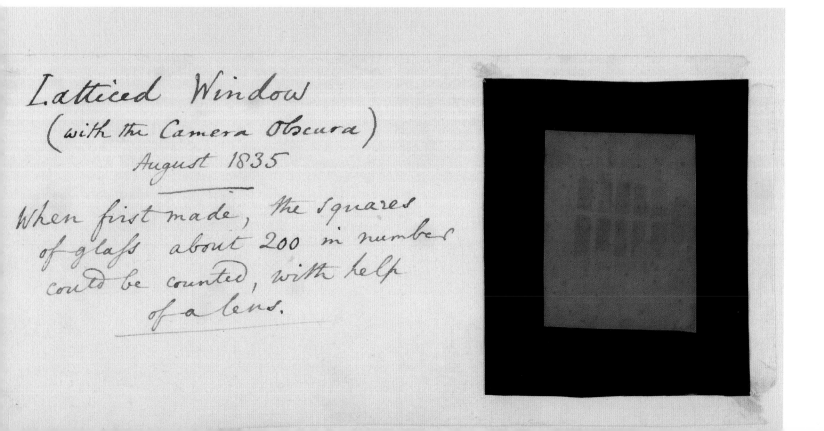

George Eastman (1854-1932)

The man who made a fortune by bringing photography to the masses was American George Eastman. In the early 1880s, he was joint owner of a company that made glass photographic plates. For most people, boxes of heavy and fragile glass plates were inconvenient to carry around for long, so they were reluctant to take up photography as a hobby.

In 1888, Eastman introduced the first roll-film camera. This was a simple box camera that came complete with a 100-exposure roll of paper-based film. A year later, Eastman introduced transparent film of higher quality. Eastman's cameras were very popular, and the firm expanded rapidly, becoming the Eastman Kodak Company in 1892.

In 1900, the year the company was incorporated, Eastman Kodak introduced a roll-film camera that was much cheaper than previous models. With the 'Brownie' camera priced at only $1, large numbers were sold and the Eastman Kodak company soon established itself as a major supplier of photographic equipment. By 1924, Eastman had accumulated a fortune of nearly $200 million, and gave away half of it to worthy causes.

The wet process

In the 1840s, the idea of having one's picture taken by a photographer became popular, and many portrait artists whose income had started to fall opened photographic studios. The daguerreotype process was widely used because it gave such a sharp image. The calotype was relatively indistinct, the image being softened by the grain of the paper used for the negative. New cameras and lenses were introduced, and photographic materials with greater sensitivity enabled exposure times to be cut. The English sculptor Frederick Scott Archer invented the collodion process in 1851. This gave the clarity of the daguerreotype process combined with the convenience of the collotype by using glass negatives to make prints on paper. The great disadvantage was that it was a wet process – inconvenient because the photographer had to sensitize the plates in a solution immediately before exposure, and develop the image straight away. Nevertheless, the collodion system soon became the generally preferred process, and English photographer Roger Fenton used it in 1855 to produce photographs of the Crimean war, developing his pictures in a portable darkroom, sometimes while under fire.

Photographers travelled abroad to take photographs, as the public had become eager to see realistic pictures of people and scenes from distant lands, rather than the impressions of painters. Added reality became possible in 1851, when Scottish inventor David Brewster invented a stereoscope suitable for viewing photographs. Two photographs, taken by cameras a small distance apart, were viewed together to give a three-dimensional effect. Later, special cameras designed for stereoscopic work were introduced. Brewster's instrument was based on an invention, made some 20 years earlier, by English physicist Charles Wheatstone.

Dry plates and roll film

In 1871, English doctor Richard Maddox thought of a way to overcome the disadvantage of the collodion process. Instead of wet plates, his system used dry plates with a layer of gelatin containing the light-sensitive chemicals. In 1878, this process came on the market, thus enabling photographers to take pictures without having to have darkroom equipment available all the time.

American manufacturer George Eastman made a most significant contribution to photography in 1888, when he introduced his Kodak – the first roll-film camera. No longer did the photographer have to carry heavy piles of fragile glass plates. The first roll film had a paper backing, but Eastman changed to using transparent film the following year. Its chemical coating was sensitive enough to allow 'snapshots' to be taken in bright light. This, the cheapness of the camera and the convenience of the roll film, ensured that photography soon became a popular hobby.

Colour

The first colour photograph was taken in 1861 by English photographer Thomas Sutton, working with Scottish physicist James Clerk Maxwell, who invented the process. Photographs of a coloured ribbon were taken through red, green and blue colour filters and used to produce separate

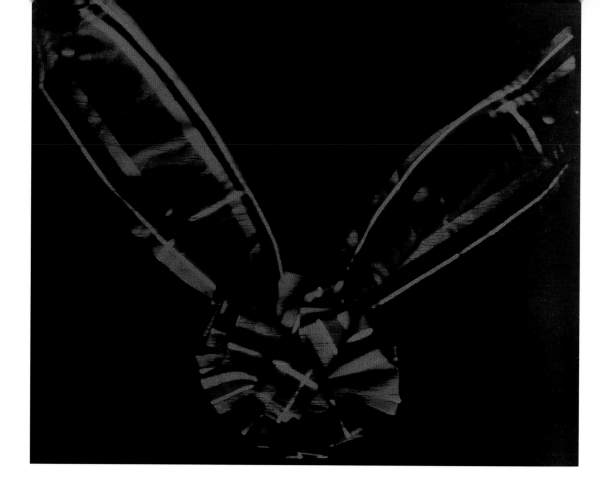

above The first colour photograph, taken by Thomas Sutton in 1861, using a process invented by James Clerk–Maxwell. Separate exposures were made to record the red, green and blue content. These were combined by projection to produce a full-colour image.

black-and-white transparencies representing these colours. When the transparencies were projected through colour filters, the images combined to form a full-colour picture on the screen.

In 1904, French brothers Auguste and Louis Lumière invented the first successful single-plate colour process. Colour photography then became available to the general public but, even in the early 1950s, most people were still taking black-and-white photographs as colour materials were relatively expensive.

The two main types of colour photography processes used today produce colour prints or transparencies, the latter commonly used as slides. As in black-and-white photography, the prints are made by a negative-positive process. Transparencies are made by a technique called reversal. A negative image is first developed on the film, which is then exposed to white light. The original image is bleached out and a positive image formed by further development. This is then fixed to produce a permanent positive transparency.

Instant pictures

American Edwin H Land invented the Polaroid Land camera in 1947. This first instant-picture camera contained a capsule of processing paste, which enabled a black-and-white photograph to be produced within a minute of pressing the shutter. Land introduced an instant colour camera in 1963. The latest electronic digital cameras allow the results to be seen immediately on a screen. The stored picture data can be transferred to a computer system for digital printing or for use in electronic documents.

Moving pictures

While photography was in its early stages of development, several inventors were experimenting with systems for producing moving pictures. Flicking a succession of slightly different drawings before the eyes gave the impression of a single moving picture, and various machines were made to demonstrate this effect. One such toy was the thaumatrope, built in 1826 by English inventor Henry Fitton. Other inventions of this kind included the phenakistoscope (1833), zoetrope (1860) and praxinoscope (1877). Meanwhile, photography had progressed, and it was not long before photographs replaced the drawings and painted images in these early machines.

English photographer Edward Muggeridge, better known by his adopted name of Eadweard Muybridge, moved to California and, from 1872, studied the movements of animals in motion. Each study, used a large number of cameras fitted with high-speed shutters to take a sequence of still pictures in rapid succession. The results obtained with a galloping horse astonished people, many of whom refused to believe the evidence before them, for the pictures were so unlike the conventional representations of moving horses in paintings. To dispel doubt, Muybridge built a projector to show the pictures rapidly, one after another. And that is how, in the 1880s, audiences at his lectures in the United States and Europe, were treated to their first short, flickering movies.

above The Agfa ePhoto 1280 digital camera. The use of electronic storage in cameras means that pictures can be viewed immediately without chemical processing. The camera has a built-in screen, and the pictures can be transferred to a computer for printing, or for use in electronic documents.

left The phenakistoscope, invented in the early 1830s, was a toy that gave the illusion of a moving image when still pictures on a spinning disc were viewed in quick succession through slots in another disc.

Cameras and projectors

In 1882, French inventor Etienne-Jules Marey invented a camera specially designed to take a rapid succession of still pictures on a single glass plate in order to study the movement of birds in flight. He later produced a camera that took a series of pictures on the new paper-backed film. From the late 1890s, American inventor Thomas Alva Edison and many others built movie cameras and projectors. One of the most successful of the early systems was first demonstrated publicly in 1895 by its inventors, the Lumière brothers. They toured the world demonstrating their lightweight combined camera-projector, which used film with sprocket holes down the sides, like that used today.

Talking pictures

The early movies were silent, with captions to indicate what was being said, and a pianist who tried to reflect the mood of the on-screen action. With the development of electronics, film companies experimented with ways of providing films with their own sound tracks. *The Jazz Singer* (1927) was mostly silent, but audiences were thrilled when the pictures on screen suddenly appeared to talk and sing. The first film with synchronized sound throughout was *The Lights of New York* (1928).

Since those days, developments in the film industry have included wide-screen presentations, 3D films and multitrack stereo sound. Most home movie enthusiasts now use tape, rather than film, and can play back the pictures from their camcorders on a TV set. But nothing since has matched the sheer excitement of that day in 1927 when the pictures started to talk.

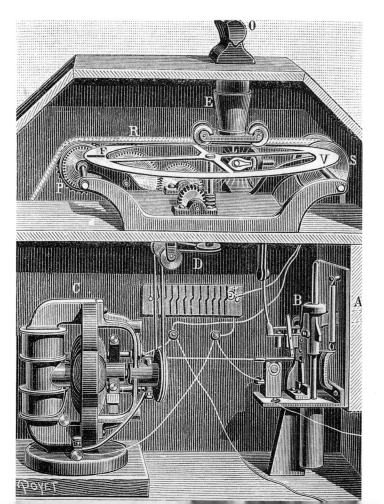

left Thomas Edison and William Dickson caused a sensation when they demonstrated their Kinetoscope to the public in 1894. A series of photographs on a strip of film were presented in rapid successsion so a realistic moving picture was seen in the viewer.

above right Making *The Jazz Singer*, the 1927 Al Jolson film that featured sections with synchronised sound. Film makers were quick to exploit the opportunity this gave them, and produced a stream of musicals with sound throughout.

right When filming in daylight, artificial lighting is commonly used to brighten the shadow areas and thus reduce the contrast between the brightest and darkest parts of the image. This enables the film to show detail in all parts of the scene.

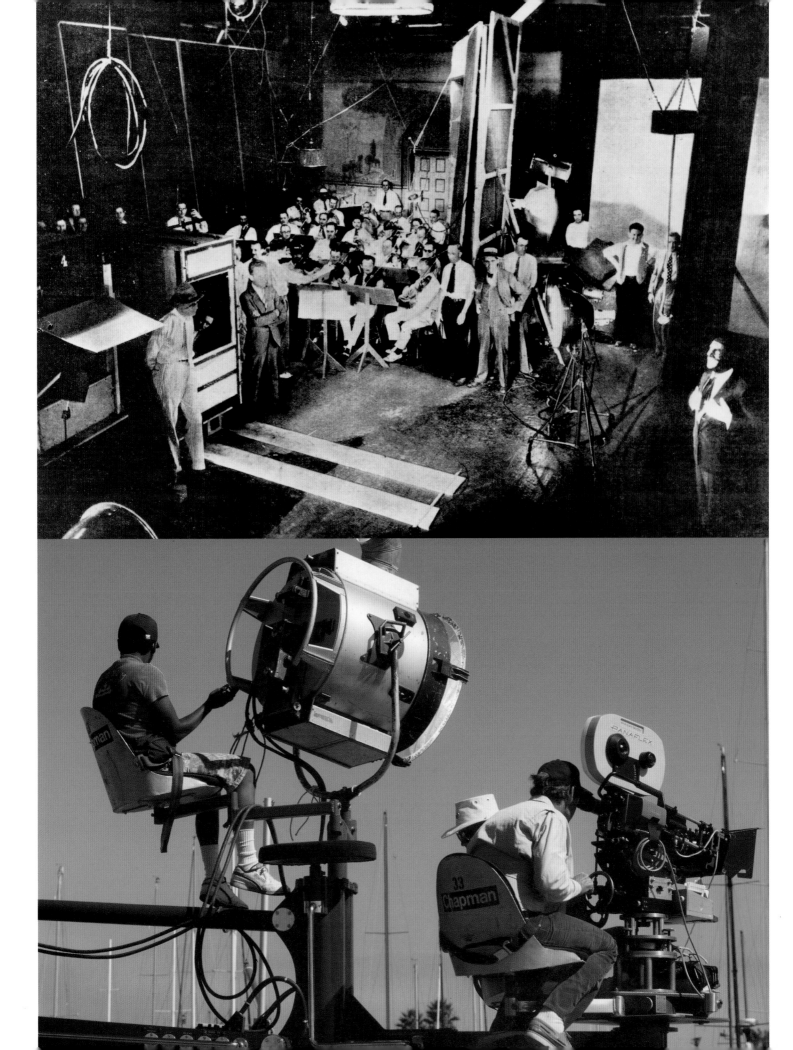

domestic appliances

11

11

previous Developments in technology mean that designers and engineers regularly reinvent familiar household articles such as the vacuum cleaner.

above and far right The paraffin (kerosine) lamp became popular in the 1860s when, with the development of oil wells, the fuel became available at low cost.

Of all the appliances found in the home, the most important are concerned with lighting and heating, and this has been the case since people first found a cave they liked and decided to stay. People generally started to settle around 8000 BC, soon after they had learnt how to start fires. Besides providing light and heat inside caves, fire also enabled people to start cooking some foods, and this led to the development of cooking pots and other equipment.

Friction and sparks

By 7000 BC, some people had reliable ways of making fire by rubbing sticks together, or by striking flint against iron pyrites to produce sparks, although, even by the 20th Century, some primitive tribes had still not discovered these methods, and had to keep a flame burning constantly. In Europe, fires were lit for centuries using a kit contained in a tinder box. Flint and steel were the materials struck together to produce sparks, and these ignited the tinder, which often consisted of charred linen. The flame was then transferred by means of a wooden splint. The wheel tinder box had a serrated disc that rubbed against a fixed flint to make sparks. A similar arrangement was used in cigarette lighters, developed from the 1800s, although the modern 'flint' is actually a form of the alloy misch metal.

Matches

Matches were invented when chemists found ways to make self-igniting splints. The first matches, invented in the early 1800s, were inconvenient and usually dangerous, involving processes such as dipping a chemically coated stick in acid, or bursting a glass capsule to allow chemicals to mix and cause ignition. English chemist John Walker invented the first friction matches in 1827. They ignited when the chemically coated tips were struck on sandpaper. Like some matches sold today, these could be ignited accidentally. In 1845, Austrian chemist Anton von Schrötter had the idea of putting just some of the chemicals on the match, and the rest on the striking surface, so that it was almost impossible to ignite a match by accident. Improved and safer chemicals were introduced later, but the same principle is used in modern safety matches.

Oil lamps

The earliest lamps, found in Iraq, were made from hollowed soft rock, and date from 80,000 BC. These would have contained vegetable oil, drawn up to the flame by a fibre wick. Candles made from animal fat can be traced back to the 900s BC. An improved oil lamp was made by Swiss inventor Aimé Argand in 1784. It had a cylindrical fabric wick with a central tube that supplied air to the inner surface, and a glass chimney to create an updraught. These features enabled more thorough combustion to take place, and produced a much brighter flame than obtained from earlier lamps. Paraffin (kerosine) for lamp fuel was manufactured from shale oil and coal tar from the 1850s, but was made from petroleum after the first successful oil well was drilled in 1859. With the fuel readily available at low cost, paraffin lamps became extremely popular from the 1860s.

Gaslight

In 1807, central London's Pall Mall became the first street to have gas lighting. Within 25 years, most of the large cities in Europe and the United States had gas lamps in their streets too, but the brighter oil lamp was still used in most homes. Then, in 1885, Austrian chemist Baron von Welsbach invented the gas mantle. He had found that fabric containing certain chemicals would glow brightly when held in a flame, and made the material into mantles to fit over the gas burners. The mantles were extremely successful and, where gas supplies were available, people started using the new lighting in preference to oil lamps. In fact, an improved mantle, introduced in 1891, worked so well that gaslight competed successfully with electric lighting for many years. By the time electricity had taken over as the main means of lighting, gas had become a widely used fuel in industry, and many people preferred gas for cooking and for heating their homes.

Electricity

The application of electricity for useful purposes has its roots in some strange experiments conducted by Italian physicist Luigi Galvani in 1786. He found that a dead frog's legs would twitch when he put a copper hook into the spine and hung the animal from iron railings. In the 1790s, Italian scientist Alessandro Volta discovered the cause to be an electric current, generated by the two different metals and the moist materials inside the frog. This led Volta to invent a battery, which became known as Volta's pile. It consisted of a stack of cells, each consisting of a silver and zinc disk, separated by material soaked in salt or alkaline solution.

From then on, scientists had a steady source of electricity for experimental and demonstration purposes. Electricity could heat a wire – a principle used today in electric heaters and incandescent lamps. When Danish physics professor Hans Oersted was demonstrating this fact in 1819, he made one of the most important discoveries in science. On connecting a wire across the terminals of a battery, he noticed that a nearby compass needle deflected from the north-south direction. When he disconnected the wire, the needle returned to its normal position. Oersted had discovered electromagnetism – the magnetic effect of an electric current. Others then developed practical electromagnets, consisting of coils wound on iron formers to increase the magnetic effect. In 1821, English scientist Michael Faraday used electromagnetism to cause a suspended wire to rotate near a strong permanent magnet. Ten years later, he showed the reverse effect – that relative movement between a wire and a permanent magnet could produce electricity. These demonstrations led to the development of two most important devices – practical electric motors and generators.

Electric lighting

In England, Humphry Davy had demonstrated the principle of the incandescent lamp as early as 1801, when he passed a current through a thin platinum filament to make it glow red hot. Unfortunately, the metal soon oxidized in the air and burnt out. Davy also made a primitive arc

Denis Papin (1647-1712)

French-born British scientist Denis Papin invented the pressure cooker and contributed to the development of the steam engine. After studying physics, Papin worked as assistant to the Dutch scientist Christiaan Huygens, who was developing an air pump. Papin later worked in London with physicist Robert Boyle, who carried out many experiments concerning the pressure and volume of gases.

In 1679, Papin found a way to make water boil at a much higher temperature than normal. He simply heated the liquid in a container with a lid that sealed it tightly. As the steam produced could not escape, the pressure inside the container increased, and this had the effect of raising the boiling point of the water from 100°C to more than 120°C. He used this principle in his pressure cooker, which was known as Papin's Digester. Food steamed in this device cooked rapidly because of the high temperature.

Experiencing the great force that the steam exerted on the lid of the container led Papin to suggest that steam could be used to push pistons in an engine. Others developed this idea to produce practical piston-operated steam engines.

lamp in 1809, using two carbon rods connected to a powerful battery. After touching the rods together briefly and then separating them slightly, a bright arc appeared between them, but a high current was drawn from the batteries, and they soon ran down. Also, the lamp was rather large, and the carbon rods had to be adjusted frequently in order to maintain the arc because they gradually wore away. Clearly, an incandescent lamp would be more convenient for general use, but the filament had to be prevented from burning out so quickly.

The obvious answer was to put the filament in a glass bulb, pump out the air and seal it. Unfortunately, the pumps available at the time were just not good enough, and left sufficient air in the bulb to oxidize the filament. When high-quality vacuum pumps became available in the mid-1870s, the problem was soon solved. In England, scientist Joseph Swan, made an incandescent lamp in 1878, based on a design he had experimented with in 1860. Its filament, made from carbon, was sealed into an evacuated glass bulb. In the USA, Thomas Alva Edison invented a similar lamp in 1879. Carbon was used in preference to metal at that time because it lasted longer when the vacuum was imperfect. Of the two inventors, it was Edison who became more closely associated with the introduction of electric lighting, because he also developed practical generators and distribution systems. In 1881, he set up a temporary power station in Holborn, London, and he built the first permanent commercial power station in 1882 in New York City.

At first, stores, hotels and places of entertainment were the main customers for the new form of lighting, most homes continuing to use gaslight, and it was not until the 1900s that the convenience of electric lighting finally won the battle for the domestic market. By then, metal filaments were used as they could give a much brighter light without burning out. The modern tungsten-filament lamp, its bulb filled with an inert gas, had been produced by 1913. Fluorescent lamps for domestic lighting became available in the late 1930s, having been developed from the gas discharge lamps used for advertising signs.

Once mains cables had been installed for providing homes with electricity, there was the added attraction of being able to use various new electrically operated labour-saving appliances too, for heating, cooking, cooling, washing, cleaning, sewing, ironing, and other tasks.

Heating and cooking

Since people had traditionally gathered around fires in the open air, they did the same in caves and then in buildings too. They warmed themselves while meat was roasted over the open fire or cooked in a pot.

Then, in the 1500s, the fire was moved to the side of the room, and a chimney was installed to take away the smoke. This became essential when the much smokier coal started to replace wood as the main fuel. Simple ovens first appeared in the 1500s too, then came various utensils and gadgets for boiling, toasting and other tasks. Unlike wood, coal had to be confined in a container, and the cooking range started to develop when an oven and stands for utensils were built around the fire. The basic design of cooking stoves was set for some 150 years when, in 1802, English ironworker George Bodley patented an enclosed cooking range. Domestic gas cookers started to become popular in the 1860s, and electric cookers in the 1920s, although both appliances had first appeared decades before.

With the arrival of these gas and electrical appliances, there was no longer the need to keep a coal fire burning all day for cooking, which was a relief in summer, but a house could become too cool in the evenings. Gas and electric fires provided the solution as, like the ovens, they could be switched on or off as required. And the fact that a thermostat provided automatic temperature control on these and other heating devices made them even more convenient.

The Roman hypocaust was one of the first forms of central heating, ducts under the floors carrying air heated by a fire. A similar idea appeared in the USA in the early 1800s, when some buildings were equipped with a boiler, arranged to circulate steam through radiators. Some later systems used hot water instead of steam, and warm-air systems were introduced in the 1900s. The heat was sometimes supplied from a boiler at the back of a fireplace, but most central heating systems now have a separate heater, fuelled by gas or oil. The heater is still called a boiler, although it no longer has to reach such a high temperature as when steam was used to convey the heat. One advantage of warm-air systems is that they can be part of a general air conditioning system, incorporating facilities for cooling too.

Cooling

Three thousand years ago, the Chinese were transferring ice, formed in winter sub-zero temperatures, to heat-insulated cellars for use through the summer, mainly for keeping food fresh. The ancient Greeks and Romans got their ice from the mountains. In 1748, Scottish physicist William Cullen used ether to demonstrate the principle of refrigeration. When the liquid was evaporated, its temperature dropped sufficiently to freeze water. Many kinds of practical refrigerator followed from the early

above In the 1990s improvements in domestic appliances concentrated on making them less wasteful to make and operate.

left After WWII, domestic appliances became more affordable, and such items as refrigerators and food mixers began to appear in more and more homes. Demonstrations like this formed part of the manufacturers' marketing techniques.

above A water closet invented in the late eighteenth century by Joseph Bramah. Early water closets date from the 1400s. Vermin and foul smells tended to rise from the drains, but Bramah's design had a water trap to prevent these problems.

Joseph Bramah (1748-1814)

English mechanical engineer credited with inventing many practical devices. Besides an improved water closet, he invented a machine for automatically numbering banknotes, an unpickable lock, a beer pump, a hydraulic press, several precision machine tools and a wood-planing machine.

Bramah was first a farm labourer, then a cabinet maker, before turning to engineering and invention. His first patent, granted in 1778, was for his water closet. Most locks that Bramah had seen were fairly easy to pick so, in 1784, he devised a complex mechanism that he thought would be impossible to open without the right key. He even offered a reward of 200 guineas (£210) to anyone who could pick it. The prize was never won, and the lock was not picked until 37 years after he died.

Bramah's lock was so secure because of its complex mechanism and, in order to make it, the inventor had to invent several high-precision machine tools. A blacksmith called Henry Maudslay assisted in their construction, and the techniques they devised helped to found the machine–tool industry. Bramah also provided training for a new generation of engineers.

left The Dyson Dual Cyclone is a modern version of an old appliance, the first vacuum cleaner having been produced in 1903. Most vacuum cleaners use a bag to trap dust, but the Dyson machines use air currents to separate out most of the dust and then filter out the finer particles.

1800s, the most successful using ammonia as the refrigerant. This process was introduced by Frenchman Ferdinand Carré in 1859, and most refrigerators and freezers used in homes today work on the same principle, although synthetic refrigerants are used instead of the toxic ammonia. The most common type of fridge has an electrically operated compressor to convert the vapourized refrigerant back into liquid again.

Gadgets

The 1800s was a period in which numerous gadgets were invented, and many old designs were improved. And the availability of electricity led to many manual machines being developed into powered models. The first vacuum cleaner, invented in 1859, needed one person to operate the pump while another used the machine to suck up the dust. Washing clothes meant agitating them in a tub by hand, and the first step in drying was to put them through the rollers of a mangle, turned by hand. The first sewing machine to become popular was invented in 1851 by American Isaac Singer, and hand and treadle-operated versions were manufactured. By the 1920s, electrically powered alternatives for all these machines were becoming popular, with manufacturers emphasising the amount of time that would be saved.

The first water closet appeared around 1460, but this kind of convenience became better known in the 1590s, when John Harington installed a flush toilet for Queen Elizabeth I in her palace at Richmond, near London. With the introduction of water traps to prevent smells coming up from the outlet, the basic principles of the modern water closet were finalised in the 1770s. But one major advance was made in an associated field in the 1880s, and it is English manufacturer Walter Alcock whom we must thank for perforated toilet paper.

12

recording sound and vision

12

previous A mixing desk in a modern recording studio. Individual controls are provided for adjusting the level and quality of up to 16 or 24 sound signals, which can be recorded separately on multitrack tape.

above An Edison phonograph made in the early 1900s. The first phonographs recorded sound vibrations on cylinders covered with tinfoil, whereas this type used wax-covered cylinders for higher quality.

Even the moderately priced audio equipment used for playing music in the home tends to be highly complex these days. Yet quite simple mechanical devices can record and playback sounds with reasonable clarity, and such devices were used for many years before the age of electronics.

Sound recording

In the 1870s, just after Alexander Graham Bell had invented the telephone, American inventor Thomas Alva Edison was trying to make a machine to record and playback sounds. It would be useful for recording Morse code telegraph signals, enabling a busy operator to translate the sounds into words at a more convenient time.

A sound recorder would also be useful as a dictating machine in general offices. The thought of recording music for entertainment does not seem to have occurred to Edison at that stage, presumably because recording speech with adequate quality was enough of a challenge to start with.

Edison knew that sounds made vibrations, and was trying to find how to record the vibrations in a form that could be changed back into sounds. For more than 20 years, other inventors had tried to solve the problem, but it was Edison who succeeded in 1877 with a machine called the phonograph.

It had a horizontal brass cylinder with a spiral groove around the outside, and this was covered with a layer of tin foil. Turning a handle made the cylinder rotate and move sideways on a screw thread. Resting lightly on the foil was a steel needle connected to a thin diaphragm. When Edison spoke into the diaphragm, the sounds made it vibrate, forcing the needle up and down as it pushed the foil into the groove on the cylinder. As a result, the needle made a series of 'hills and valleys' in the long spiral track formed in the foil. Edison played back this crude sound recording using the same equipment. The undulations in the foil made the needle move up and down, and this vibrated the diaphragm, causing it to reproduce the sounds. As Edison turned the handle to replay the first recording, the diaphragm crackled, but the words he had chosen for this historic moment were quite distinct: 'Mary had a little lamb – its fleece was white as snow. . .'

Many problems had to be solved to develop this interesting novelty into a useful machine. Unwanted sounds could accidentally be added to the recording during playback, and the needle soon wore away the foil, making the sounds progressively weaker and more crackly with each playing. Another problem was that the needle tended to jump along the track from one microscopic hill to the next when these were very close together, thus distorting the sound. Improvements made by Edison and others soon followed, including the use of wax-coated cylinders, which gave better sound quality.

Knowing the value of good publicity, Edison arranged for the voices of famous people, including the English poet Alfred, Lord Tennyson, to be recorded on his machines. One of the first music recordings was a Hungarian rhapsody, made by its composer, Johannes Brahms.

above Thomas Alva Edison with the phonograph he invented in 1877. His numerous other inventions included a telephone equipment, an incandescent lamp, and electricity generating systems.

Discs

While the cylinder recorder was still being improved, German Emile Berliner was working on an alternative method of recording. Instead of cylinders, he used discs, which were far more convenient to make and store. Berliner introduced his Gramophone in 1887, and commercial production started in 1894. Early discs were recorded using Edison's hill-and-valley technique, but Berliner later improved the sound quality by introducing the lateral cut record, made by the recording stylus moving from side to side, rather than up and down.

In the early years of the new century, record companies were steadily improving the technology. Discs were much easier to duplicate than cylinders. Once an original recording had been cut into a wax blank, it could be copied using an electroplating technique and mass produced by pressing in shellac. In the early 1920s, commercial recordings were still made acoustically. The sounds were picked up by a large horn and fed down a tube to a disc recording machine, where they made a cutting stylus vibrate. To achieve a reasonable sound balance when recording music, the quietest instruments had to be positioned close to the mouth of the horn. Recordings made by the acoustic process are easily identified as they sound just as you were listening through a long tube which, in a way, you are. But, bearing in mind how primitive the equipment was, the best of these acoustic recordings were a remarkable achievement.

With the development of electronics, new recording equipment became available around 1925. Microphones replaced the acoustic horn, and the sound signals were balanced on a mixer before being amplified and fed to an electrical cutting head. The resulting improvement in quality

above Separating a metal matrix, formed by electroplating, from a metal master — one stage in the manufacture of a gramophone record. The matrix is used to make the stampers, which are used to press the final records from vinyl.

was impressive, although the public could not appreciate it fully because most people continued to use acoustic gramophones for many years. In fact, clockwork wind-up gramophones, with an acoustic pickup called a sound box and a small built-in horn, were still on sale in some record stores in the mid-1950s. But, by then, other major improvements in recording technology were luring people away from the equipment that had served them well for so many years.

Hi-Fi and stereophonic sound

'High-fidelity' records were the result of several developments made in the 1940s. Record companies started pressing their discs in vinyl, which gave much less background hiss than shellac (and had the added advantage of being almost unbreakable). In Britain, Decca introduced the technique of recording the widest possible frequency range and, in the United States, Columbia introduced the long-playing record, or LP. Until then, listening to a recording of a long orchestral work had meant getting up to change the disc every few minutes. The LP, with its slow speed and smaller groove, lasted much longer and made playing records a less energetic activity. And, with the introduction of stereophonic sound, listeners could, at last, settle back and imagine they were hearing a live performance, rather than a recording. Harvey Fletcher, American physicist and expert in acoustics, gave the first public demonstration of stereophonic sound in 1934, and its introduction to the commercial recording industry was a major advance in recording technology.

The original idea of stereophonic recordings was to present the ears with the two, slightly different sound patterns that they would hear at a live performance. A pair of microphones, slightly separated or pointing at different angles, picked up the sounds. On the disc, the two signals were recorded separately in the walls of the groove. A special pickup with two sensors was used to detect the signals, which were then amplified and reproduced on a pair of separated loudspeakers.

While some record producers and engineers attempted to use stereophonic sound to make their recordings as realistic as possible, others used the technology to obtain new effects. With suitable (some would say unsuitable) microphone placing, a piano could be made to fill the 'sound stage', with the lowest notes coming from the extreme left and the top notes from the far right. It was as if the listener was sitting on the pianist's lap! When recording groups of musicians, some engineers starting using a single microphone for each instrument, or group of instruments, so that the relative volumes could be adjusted for the best balance. Each signal produced in this way was electronically split between the left and right stereo channels and could be made to sound as if it came from any desired direction.

left A recording session in progress. Individual instruments, or sections of the orchestra, are recorded on separate tracks of a tape. The final sound balance is determined later, when the tracks are combined to produce a stereo master tape.

below Although domestic recorders generally use small cassettes of tape, professional recorders still use reel-to-reel tape. Common widths are quarter–inch, half–inch, inch and two–inch, the larger sizes being used for multitrack recording.

Tape recording

The forerunner of tape recording was a system invented in 1898 by Danish engineer Valdemar Poulson. His telegraphone was designed for recording telegraph signals as magnetic patterns on steel wire. Wire recorders were later used for sound recording, but better results were obtained with steel tape, and then tapes with magnetic oxide coatings. These were developed in the United States and Germany in the 1920s and 1930s. In the late 1940s, tape recording became popular with commercial recording companies, and many enthusiasts in the 1950s owned open-reel machines, which they used mainly for recording radio programmes and copying commercial records. These machines were mostly monophonic, as few people could afford the extra expense of stereophonic equipment.

Domestic tape equipment became more popular in the 1960s, with the spread of cartridges and cassettes. Cartridges contained a very long tape loop and were popular for providing background music, most of which was supplied prerecorded. Cassettes provided a more compact and convenient means of recording than the open-reel machines had done, and soon few people wanted anything else. Improved production techniques had reduced costs, and stereo became standard.

Multitrack

In professional studios, tape machines had progressed from mono to stereo models and then multitrack. By the 1970s, machines capable of recording 16 or more separate sounds provided engineers with increased flexibility. In many cases, the recording session became merely an exercise in getting the sounds onto tape. This reduced production costs because the musicians did not have to remain until all the technical aspects had been dealt with. Sometimes just a few performers would stay behind to re-record their parts while listening to a replay of the other tracks on the tape. Musicians did not even have to meet in order to participate in the same recording, as the multitrack tape could be sent away for others to add their contribution in another studio – sometimes in another country. The creative part of the producer's job – mixing and balancing the instruments to reduce the multitrack recording to a pair of stereo signals on a master tape – took place later. The master recording was then used to produce the final discs or tapes.

Eliminating hiss

One of the main problems that has bothered hi-fi enthusiasts is the hiss that can be heard behind recordings. Various methods have been used to reduce or eliminate this, notably the Dolby noise reduction system. In a professional version, all low level sounds are increased in strength before being recorded.

On replay, all low-level sounds are reduced in strength. This ensures that all the wanted low level sounds are reproduced at the correct level, while any unwanted low-level sounds introduced during the recording are reduced in level. In practice, the main effect is on tape hiss, which is reduced so much as to make it virtually inaudible. A simplified form of the Dolby noise reduction system is provided on many high-quality domestic cassette recorders.

Another way of reducing tape hiss is to do away with tape altogether. Although we tend to associate discs with crackly recordings, this is more to do with old recording materials or badly cared-for discs than with the capabilities of the medium. A modern disc can, in fact, give lower background noise than tape, and some recordings of classical music have been made by recording directly onto disc. This technique lacks the flexibility provided by multitrack recording, but musicians, knowing that corrections cannot be made, concentrate more on their work, and some say that this results in a better performance. Of course, the final tapes and discs used by the consumer will not be up to the same high standard as the studio masters, and will soon deteriorate if treated carelessly.

Digital recording is another method of reducing hiss and other unwanted noise. In ordinary analogue recording, the unwanted sounds are in the same form as the wanted sounds – both are present as changes in amplitude, or strength. But, if the wanted sounds are encoded and recorded as a series of pulses, these can be retrieved by circuits that do not detect any noise introduced by the recording system. Some ordinary records were made from digital master tapes from the 1970s. Today, high quality analogue recorders are still used in studios, but the final product is usually in the form of a digital recording on a compact disc (CD). The small plastic disc has the sound signals recorded as a series of microscopic pits in a highly reflective surface. On replay, the pits scatter the light from a láser beam, whereas the unaltered surface reflects the beam back to a detector. The output from the detector is therefore a digital (on/off) signal that can be used to reconstruct the original sound signal.

Other recording systems now available include digital audio tape (dat) and dvd (digital versatile disc). As well as sounds, the latter can be used to store computer data, still pictures and video recordings.

Video recorders

Audio tape recorders store sound signals as magnetic patterns applied by special electromagnets called recording heads. It is more difficult to retain high-frequency signals on tape as the patterns are packed together more tightly and tend to demagnetize one another. The solution is to record at a higher tape-to-head speed so that the patterns are more spread out along the tape. The video signals corresponding to television pictures contain frequencies higher than those of audio signals, so a high tape-to-head speed is required to record the pictures. In early video recorders, the tape moved so rapidly through the machine that it was liable to break. The practical solution was to have the tape moving relatively slowly while a set of recording heads on a rapidly rotating drum laid down the video signals as a series of stripes diagonally across the tape. In this way, a high tape-to-head speed was achieved without risk of the tape breaking. By the 1990s, domestic videotape recorders had became extremely popular for taping television programmes and, for recording holidays and other events, many people had discarded their still camera in favour of a camcorder – a combined TV camera and videotape machine.

above A film dubbing studio, where sounds can be added to the original soundtrack of a film. Sound Effects diffficult to record on location may be made by improvised means, and all the speech of a foreign film may be re-recorded in the local language.

13

medical technology

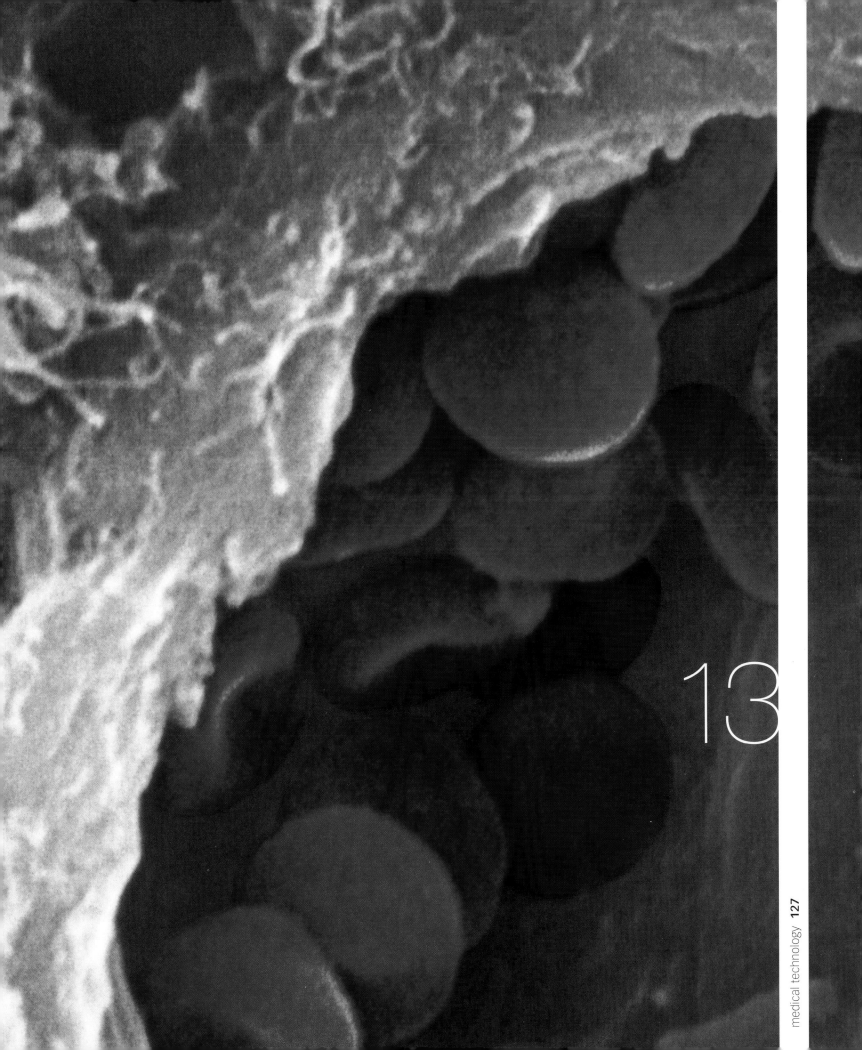

13

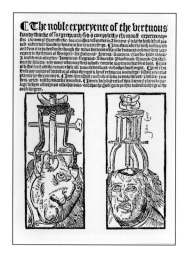

above An illustration from a book published in 1525 — *The noble experence of the vertuous handy warke of surgeri*. It shows trephining, or trepanning — the cutting of a hole in the skull to cure an illness.

previous Developments in medical technology have obvious effects on our lives, making diagnosis of conditions more accurate and care of patients more sophisticated, so improving our quality of life.

Medicine was a simple matter in prehistoric times. Common ailments, such as colds and constipation, could be treated with herbal remedies. Unusual illnesses were generally regarded as the work of a devil or the revenge of a god who had been displeased. Some believed that an evil spirit had entered the body, while others thought that the person's soul had been removed. Witch doctors and other medicine men could be called in to devise a cure, which often involved administering a drug during a ritualized ceremony. If that failed, a hole could be cut in the patient's skull to allow the evil spirit to escape, or the soul to re-enter the body. The hole, about three or four centimetres across, was cut with a stone tool. This technique, called trephining or trepanning, was carried out in parts of Europe, Africa and South America. Fossilized skulls dating back to 8000 BC show holes that healed, and indicate that some patients did live for years after such an operation. For a few people, this was probably the most suitable treatment and, even today, surgeons sometimes cut a hole in the skull to relieve pressure on a patient's brain.

A scientific approach

The ancient Egyptians made great advances in medicine in the 3rd Millennium BC. Physicians started to specialize and write down their methods for treating various diseases, fractures and wounds. In the first century AD, a Greek physician called Galen of Pergamum made great contributions to medicine as a science, especially in the fields of anatomy and surgery, by conducting experiments on animals and recording the results. In those times, the dissection of human corpses was not generally acceptable, and Galen made many incorrect assumptions about the human body. Nevertheless, his teachings had great influence, and it was not until the 1500s that his errors concerning human anatomy began to be corrected.

Around 1500, the Italian Leonardo da Vinci dissected many corpses in order to study human anatomy, and produced hundreds of drawings showing the structure of the body. An Italian doctor called Andreas Vesalius also used the dissection of corpses to advance his knowledge and, in 1543, published the first textbook on human anatomy. The English physician William Harvey studied the human circulation system in the early 1600s and explained the functions of the heart, arteries and veins.

right A leg being amputated in the 1500s. The assistant with the padded glove had the task of punching the patient in the head until he was unconscious, for anaesthetics were unknown in those days.

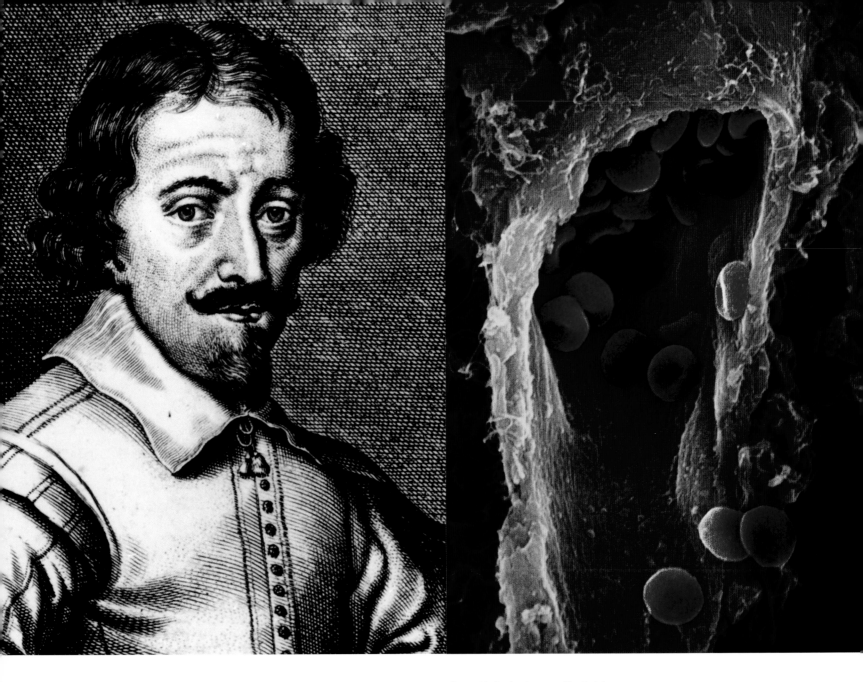

above Zacharias Janssen, the Dutch optician often credited with inventing the compound (multi-lens) microscope. He did establish the basic design, but it was not until the 1800s that this microscope was developed into a precision instrument.

above right Red blood cells, displayed by a modern scanning electron microscope with a magnification of x1,400. The first electron microscopes were developed in the 1930s.

Microscopes

Detailed examination of body tissues and fluids became possible in the 1600s with the development of the microscope. Magnifying glasses consisting of glass spheres filled with water had been used since around 2000 BC, and solid glass lenses had been available since the 1200s. It was probably a Dutch spectacle maker called Zacharias Janssen who, in the late 1500s, invented the first compound (two-lens) microscope. Although the principle of the instrument had been established, the poor quality of the lenses resulted in distorted images, especially if a high degree of magnification was used. Much better images were obtained in the 1600s by another Dutchman, Anton van Leeuwenhoek, using a simple microscope containing a single powerful lens. It was known that a drop of water placed in a small wire loop could produce great magnification, but van Leeuwenhoek had discovered how to grind good-quality high-power lenses from glass. In 1674, using his simple microscope, he became the first person to observe bacteria, and he went on to reveal the structure of spermatozoa in 1677, and red blood cells in 1684.

The compound microscope had more potential, but suffered particularly from chromatic aberration – blurring of the image by colour fringes. It was Chester Moor Hall's invention of the achromatic lens in 1773 that enabled the production of high-quality compound microscopes with little colour fringing. Other inventors then gradually developed the optical microscope into a precision instrument, thus providing the medical profession with a highly important tool for studying the microorganisms that cause disease.

Immunology

From the ages of 13 to 21, Edward Jenner was apprenticed to a surgeon and, in 1771, joined St George's Hospital, London, where he increased his knowledge of medicine and biology. Two years later, he returned to his home town of Berkeley, Gloucestershire, to practice medicine. At that time, outbreaks of smallpox were common, and frequently fatal.

Protection could be provided by the old oriental technique of inoculation – deliberately infecting a healthy person with a mild form of the disease. However, many people were reluctant to be given this 'protection', as it often proved fatal and helped to spread the disease further. Jenner was determined to perfect a treatment based on a fact that he had learned during his apprenticeship: people who had contracted the related and fairly harmless disease of cowpox could never suffer from smallpox.

In 1796, Jenner inoculated a young boy with infected matter from cowpox sores on a dairymaid's finger. The boy duly caught the disease. Jenner then tried to infect the boy with smallpox, but he proved to be immune. Jenner's work did not meet with universal approval, and was largely ignored at first but, as the threat of smallpox was steadily overcome, it became clear that he had developed a most important technique, and vaccines were eventually produced to protect people from a wide range of serious diseases.

Anaesthetics

For centuries, patients needing to have a damaged limb removed, or their body cut open for medical treatment, were likely to die as a result of the operation. They suffered a great deal, for there were no fully effective anaesthetics or pain killers, and infections were easily picked up from the surgeons' instruments. Various substances, such as opium and alcohol, had been given to patients in attempts to relieve pain during operations, but none was completely successful. Painless surgery might have arrived earlier than it did, as British inventor Humphrey Davy discovered the anaesthetic properties of nitrous oxide in 1799.

Unfortunately, little attention was paid to his claims at first. Then, in the 1840s, numerous experiments were carried out in the United States to see if nitrous oxide or ether could be used as an effective anaesthetic. In 1842, American surgeon Crawford Long became the first person to use ether successfully in surgery when he carried out a painless operation to remove a tumour from a patient's neck. American dentist William Morton gave a public demonstration of a similar operation in 1846. Soon ether, chloroform, nitrous oxide and cocaine came into regular use for various kinds of operation.

The liquids were administered by soaking them up with a sponge, placing this in a container, and allowing the patient to breathe in the vapour as it evaporated. The main problem was in ensuring the correct dosage, as there was a fine line between the amount of anaesthetic required to render the patient unconscious and the amount that could cause harm. In the 1880s, surgeons started using less hazardous local anaesthetics, a drug being injected in the affected area and the patient remaining conscious.

Aseptic surgery

By this time, there was a better understanding of the role of bacteria in spread of disease. In 1875, English surgeon Joseph Lister had invented the antiseptic spray to combat infection. In one type, a mist of the disinfectant carbolic acid was forced into the air using a pump.

Another model used steam from a small boiler to propel the carbolic acid. Lister's original procedure of spraying the air was discontinued as it was not found to reduce infections, but carbolic acid proved effective for sterilizing wounds. Then surgeons started sterilizing their equipment and wearing masks, gowns and gloves to prevent the spread of disease, and therefore deaths resulting from surgery were immediately and dramatically reduced.

Medical equipment

Until the 1800s, doctors and surgeons had little in the way of equipment. Doctors carried a thermometer to measure a patient's temperature, and listened to the heart and lungs to check for abnormalities.

French physician René Laënnec did not like having to place his ear against a woman's chest in order to listen to her heart, although other doctors were quite willing to undertake this task. In 1816, Laënnec tried using a roll of paper to transmit the sounds to his ear and found this made the heartbeats much clearer. He then produced a more robust instrument consisting of a wide wooden tube with a tapering end piece for picking up the sounds from specific areas. In the 1850s, this simple instrument evolved into a form resembling the modern stethoscope, with twin earpieces and flexible tubing.

The 1850s saw other important developments in medical equipment. The ophthalmoscope, for examining the interior of the eye, was invented in 1851 by German scientist Hermann von Helmholtz. And, in 1853, French physician Gabriel Pravaz invented a device that was to become one of the most widely used in medicine – the hypodermic syringe.

In 1866, the English physician Thomas Allbutt invented the clinical thermometer. This responded more quickly than an ordinary thermometer, and also retained the reading until the mercury in it was shaken back down the tube.

In the late 1700s, experimenters with electricity had shown that muscular movements were associated with electric currents. Frogs' legs could be made to twitch by passing a current through them. And, in a gruesome experiment, a murderer's corpse had been hacked down from the gallows and electricity passed through it in an effort to bring about a resurrection. The chest expanded, the legs twitched, and the facial muscles forced a weird smile, but the body became still again when the supply was switched off. It was not until the 1900s that doctors perfected the technique of administering short but powerful electric shocks from the electrodes of a defibrillator to restart a patient's heart.

In 1879, English physiologist Augustus Waller adopted the opposite approach and measured the electrical impulses produced by a living person's heart. This led to the development of the electrocardiograph for checking heart condition.

In 1895, Italian Scipione Roci invented the sphygmomanometer – a simple, portable instrument for measuring a patient's blood pressure. It worked by pumping up a rubber cuff around the patient's arm to counteract the pressure exerted by the blood.

The most important event in the 1890s occurred in that same year,

above Early aids for hearing loss, such as this ear trumpet, simply magnified what sounds were able to reach the ear drum.

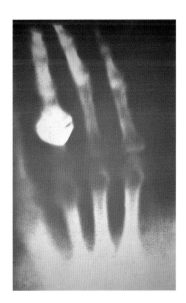

when German physicist Wilhelm Roentgen discovered X-rays. At the time, he was experimenting with an early form of cathode-ray tube – a partially evacuated glass tube through which an electric current could pass as a beam of electrons. Roentgen found that a mineral near the tube started to glow, and photographic plates became fogged. He rightly assumed that invisible rays were coming from the tube and, knowing little about them, called them simply X-rays. He found that this strange radiation passed through some substances more easily than through others, and that he could record shadowy images of objects by placing them between the tube and a photographic plate. One of these first X-ray pictures shows his wife's hand, with the bones structure clearly revealed.

above left Wilhelm Roentgen using X-ray equipment to examine a young patient. Decades passed before the harmful effects of X-rays were fully understood, and many patients developed cancer as a result of over-exposure to the radiation.

above The first X-ray picture of part of the human body. It was taken by Wilhelm Roentgen in 1895, and shows his wife's hand, part of which is obscured by her wedding ring.

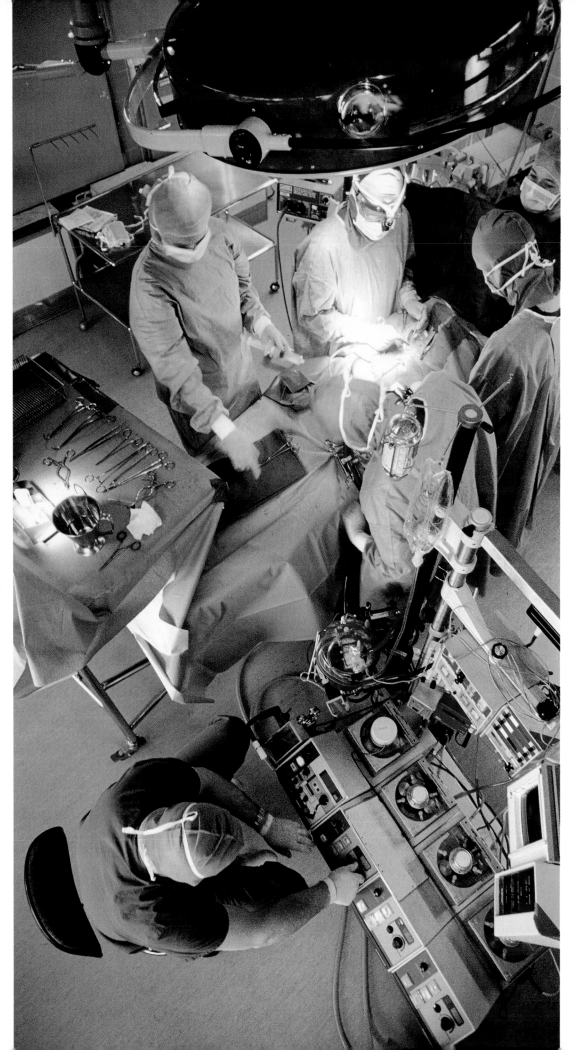

left A modern operating theatre is equipped with extensive monitoring equipment for checking on the patient's condition. Since the 1920s, the development of electronics has led to the introduction of many new tools for diagnosis and treatment.

Twentieth century technology

Roentgen's discovery of X-rays was to revolutionize the diagnosis of injury and disease, and the event also marked the first application of electronics to medicine. For his efforts, Roentgen was rewarded in 1901 with the first Nobel Prize for Physics. Another prize winner was Dutch physiologist Willem Einthoven who, in 1903, invented a sensitive galvanometer for detecting the electrical activities of the heart muscles. This led him to develop the practical electrocardiograph, and he was rewarded with the Nobel Prize for Physiology or Medicine in 1924. Five years after that, a German called Hans Berger invented a similar machine, called the electroencephalograph, for recording electrical impulses produced in the brain. This has proved to be a valuable diagnostic aid in cases of head injury and nervous system disorders.

In 1928, American physicians Philip Drinker and Louis Shaw invented the iron lung machine to assist breathing. The patient was shut into a tank with just the head protruding, and then a pump lowered the pressure inside. This allowed the chest to expand, thus causing air to be drawn through the mouth and nose and into the lungs. The pressure in the tank was then increased, forcing the chest to contract and to expel the air from the lungs.

Following experiments in the late 1920s, the first electron microscopes were developed in the early 1930s. These used beams of electrons instead of light rays and were capable of much greater magnification than optical instruments. Researchers could therefore study biological processes and structures in greater detail, thus aiding the development of medical science.

A heart-lung machine was first used in 1953 by US surgeon John Gibbon. The machine kept the patient's circulation going while Gibbon performed a heart operation, and also maintained a supply of oxygen in the blood. Although the heart-lung machine could be used safely for a few hours, it would spoil the blood if used for a prolonged period.

The first kidney transplant took place in that same year, heart pacemakers appeared in the 1960s, and heart transplantation started in 1967. Transplantation presented various problems, and many doctors felt the need instead for an artificial heart designed for continual use. The first such device was implanted into a patient in 1982. Unfortunately, he died 112 days after the operation, and improvements in the technology were slow in coming. Modern artificial hearts are more reliable, but much work still needs to be done to find materials that will operate for very long periods without deteriorating and without causing rejection by the body.

Modern medical equipment includes various kinds of scanners for producing images of internal organs. Ultrasound scans are often used to check progress during pregnancy, as the high-frequency sound waves are less likely to cause harm than exposure to X-rays. Computerized axial tomography produces X-ray images of slices through the body. In magnetic resonance imaging, similar results are obtained with the patient lying inside a powerful magnet while the body is stimulated by radio waves. These cause the various tissues to radiate different signals, which can be mapped by a computer. This technique allows neurologists to study the brain without exposing it to X-rays.

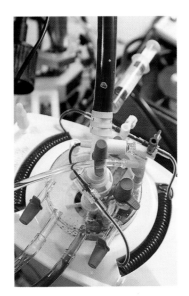

left A heart-lung machine, which maintains a patient's circulation during heart surgery. The equipment also provides the blood with oxygen, the function normally carried out by the lungs.

below An ultrasound scan showing a baby in the womb. For pre-natal checks, high-frequency supersonic waves are now generally used instead of X-rays to avoid subjecting the mother and child to frequent doses of potentially harmful radiation.

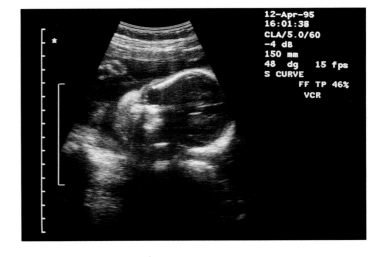

14 weapons

14

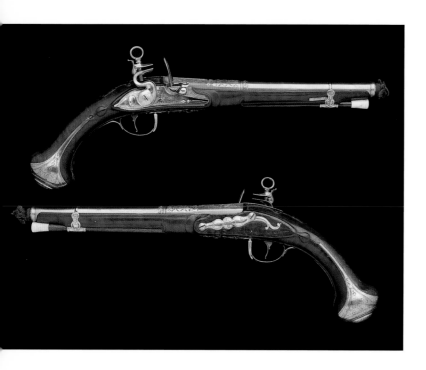

Since prehistoric times, developing and improving weapons has been one of man's main preoccupations. When it came to hunting animals and settling personal and tribal conflicts, the earliest people found it advantageous to use sticks and stones as weapons. Stones, handy for hitting at close quarters, were more useful as missiles, making it possible to gain the advantage of surprise by striking from a distance. Heavy sticks served as clubs, but slimmer ones were eventually sharpened and made into spears for thrusting or throwing. Specially shaped throwing sticks, called boomerangs, although generally associated with Australian aborigines, were developed in many regions. The kind used for hunting and fighting was non-returning, the curved path of the returning type making it too difficult to aim accurately.

Spears and blades

As people gradually learned to make and use tools, they developed the spear into a more effective weapon. A stone, chipped away to produce a sharp point, was bound to the end of the stick; later, bronze and then iron tips were attached. When face-to-face with an enemy, the side with the longer spears had an advantage. As a result, the spear developed into the pike, with its thick, metal-tipped wooden shaft, sometimes as much as six metres long. From the 600s BC, ancient Greek pikemen made a very close, square formation called a phalanx, with pikes extended at the front. This tactic, involving several hundred men, was used in both offensive and defensive situations. Two further developments were the lance, carried in the Middle Ages by mounted warriors, and the halberd, used by foot soldiers – notably Swiss mercenaries. Like the legendary Swiss Army knife, the halberd was a multi-purpose device having, in this case, a point for stabbing, a blade for hacking, and a hook for removing riders from horses' saddles.

The Bronze Age technology that produced metal points for spears from about 3500 BC also led to the manufacture of swords and daggers, which were more effective than spears at close quarters. Most swords were made of iron by about 1000 BC, as this was much harder than bronze. Swords became less effective as weapons in the 1600s, when firearms appeared on the battlefield. However, swords continued to be carried by some mounted soldiers until the 1900s, when increased fire-power, tanks and armoured vehicles finally eliminated mounted forces from the battlefield.

Slings and arrows

By 20,000 years ago, inventors had devised the first aids for firing missiles. The spear thrower, or atlatl, was a stick held in the hand and whipped forward to hurl a spear from a slot at high speed. It enabled a skilled hunter to fell the largest animals. The becket was a cord used as a sling for hurling spears. The more common kind of sling – a leather holder with attached cords – was whirled by hand and, when one cord was released, send a rock hurtling at high speed. This weapon appeared on the battlefield until the 1600s, by which time it was being used for throwing grenades. Various kinds of catapult date back to prehistoric times too.

above A pair of Spanish holster pistols, made in the late 1700s by Francisco Targarona of Madrid. Until the introduction of percussion firing devices in the 1800s, wind and rain could blow away or dampen the detonating charge.

previous The devastation of Hiroshima, after the atom-bombing of this Japanese city by the United States in August 1945. More than 70,000 people were killed. Hiroshima is now a centre for a movement aimed at banning nuclear weapons.

Most were powered by the tension in a springy wooden beam or tightly twisted cord. The Romans developed a large twisted-cord catapult, called a ballista, that could hurl a 25kg rock well over 400 metres.

Blowpipes, or blowguns, appeared in various regions, notably Southeast Asia, and South and Central America. These weapons were commonly made from hollowed cane, such as bamboo but, in some places, grooves were carved in two wooden strips, and then bound together. Another method was to drill or burn out a hole in a strip of wood using a metal tool. The length ranged from about half a metre to around seven metres, the longer type being more powerful because the pressure of the air blast acted on the projectile for longer. Such weapons were used almost exclusively for hunting, the missiles ranging from small clay pellets to short darts and up to arrows over one metre long. Poison, prepared from various plant and animal sources, was applied to the tips of darts used against larger animals in order to disable them. The best-known of these poisons was curare, obtained from a South American vine.

Although various forms of bow and arrow date from prehistoric times, it was not until the 900s AD that the crossbow was made from metal and became a highly effective weapon. It could be kept in the cocked position until the trigger was pulled to release a metal bolt. The English longbow, which fired wooden arrows, appeared in the 1300s. This powerful weapon could be fired at a much faster rate than the crossbow, but more practice was needed if high accuracy was to be achieved. Both these weapons had a range of roughly 300 metres and, on the battlefield, competed with guns until about 1500.

Fire power

Although man's mastery of fire helped to establish settlements, it also provided a powerful weapon of destruction. As long as the wind did not

above A rare Winchester .44 W.C.F. Model 1873 lever–action repeating rifle. This particular gun was once used by Annie Oakley, the 'Little Sure Shot' who starred in Buffalo Bill's Wild West Show.

Sir Hiram Maxim (1840-1916)

American-born inventor and engineer Sir Hiram Stevens Maxim is best known for his invention of the first fully automatic machine gun. This son of a farmer became an apprentice carriage maker, and later worked in a shipbuilding yard. He soon turned to invention, and was especially interested in items associated with heating and lighting, including gas generating equipment and electric lighting systems. He was appointed chief engineer of the United States Electric Lighting Company, where he devised a way to make lamp filaments from carbon.

In the early 1880s, Maxim moved to London, where he set up the Maxim Gun Company and, by 1884, he had completed the gun that bears his name. The Maxim gun used the force of recoil to eject the spent shell and force a new cartridge into the chamber. This machine gun was such an effective weapon that its use became widespread. The Maxim Gun Company later became part of munitions company Vickers Limited, with Maxim as one of its directors.

Maxim also experimented with aircraft, and managed to get a steam-powered plane to take off. He realised that the lighter petrol engine would be more suitable, but he did not continue with these experiments.

In 1900, Maxim was granted British citizenship and, in 1901, he received a knighthood.

suddenly change direction, a well-planned fire in the forest could drive out animals or enemies. Anything that burned readily could be used against an enemy, and flaming arrows provided an effective means of attacking from a distance. From the late 7th Century, the Greeks had a secret weapon – a chemical mixture that would burn even in water, and was particularly effective for setting fire to enemy ships. We still do not know for certain what substances were used to make this 'Greek fire', although some components of black powder may have been present.

Black powder, the first explosive, was a mixture of powdered saltpetre (potassium nitrate), sulphur and charcoal. The Chinese probably invented it in the 900s. They used it first in fireworks and signal flares and rockets and, by the 1200s, in small rocket weapons. The term gunpowder refers to any chemical mixture used to fire a gun, but usually means black powder, which was used for over 500 years.

The first gun was probably a device invented by the Arabs in the early 1300s. A charge of black powder at the end of a tube exploded when lit and discharged an arrow. Around the same time, primitive guns were developed in Germany too, and canons that fired iron balls were known in Italy. Hand-held guns that fired round lead bullets appeared in the late 1300s. The gunpowder in the end of the metal barrel was ignited through a small touch-hole by means of a glowing cord called a match. This had been treated with saltpetre to ensure that it would not go out, even in a strong wind.

Firing mechanisms

Having to hold the gun and touch the match on the right spot was somewhat inconvenient, especially in the heat of battle. In the late 1400s, a simple mechanism was devised to solve this problem. Attached to the side of the gun was a lever, with a clip at the top for holding the glowing match. Operating the lever moved the match so that it ignited a pinch of gunpowder in a small pan next to the touch-hole. The resulting flash in the pan set off the charge in the barrel. The lever was S-shaped and, therefore, became known as a serpentine.

A disadvantage of the early firing mechanism was that the serpentine could be accidentally moved, causing the gun to fire unexpectedly. This problem was overcome by using a mechanism that locked the lever and match, releasing it to ignite the powder when a trigger was pulled. Guns using this mechanism were known as match-locks.

At night, the glow from the match could reveal a soldier's position so, in the early 1500s, a new firing mechanism was invented that did away with the match. Instead, the wheel-lock had an iron wheel with a milled edge, and this was turned against a piece of iron pyrites, the resulting sparks igniting the powder.

An even more convenient mechanism, developed around the same time, had a simple spring-loaded striker to produce the sparks. By the early 1600s, these guns used flint instead of iron pyrites, and kept the powder shielded from wind and rain until the moment of firing. The flintlock, as it became known, proved so reliable that it replaced earlier designs and remained in service until the early 1800s, when a completely new firing system was invented.

Percussion firing

John Forsyth was a Scottish Presbyterian minister who experimented with guns and ended up in the Tower of London. He went there at the invitation of the ordnance supervisor, who was interested in Forsyth's new system for firing guns. Forsyth had eliminated the need for sparks, using instead a spring-loaded striker to set off a small detonating charge of potassium chlorate. He perfected and patented his percussion-lock system in 1807, and others developed the idea, first enclosing the detonating charge in a soft metal cap. By the 1840s, the detonating charge, main charge and bullet had been combined to form a modern-style cartridge. This was loaded into the breech of the gun, rather than the muzzle, and detonated by a blow from a firing pin.

The problem with muzzle-loaders was that, if the bullet was a tight fit, it could take a long time to force down the barrel. So ample clearance was given, however, this made the gun less accurate because the bullet could be deflected slightly as it left the muzzle. It also reduced

left A Maxim gun being operated by officers of the Royal Navy's HMS *Excellent* in 1895. Water was pumped through a jacket around the gun's single barrel to stop it overheating.

the gun's effective range, as some of the expanding gases from the explosive charge escaped around the sides of the bullet.

Since the 1500s, attempts had been made to improve accuracy by a technique called rifling. Spiral grooves along the inside of the gun barrel gave the bullet a spin, and the gyroscopic effect made it more stable in flight, but a tight fit was essential for this technique to work. One solution, developed in the 1820s, was to drop a loose fitting lead bullet down the barrel and strike it with a ramrod in order to increase its diameter.

The perfection of the breech loading cartridge meant that a tight fitting bullet could be inserted with ease, thus ensuring high accuracy and fast reloading. Then, in the 1870s, after centuries in which there had been no alternative to black powder, and following decades of dangerous experimentation, a more powerful propellant was adopted. This contained a form of nitrocellulose that became known as guncotton. These developments in cartridge structure and propellant established the design of modern general-purpose ammunition.

Revolvers and repeaters

For centuries, gunsmiths had tried to find reliable ways of reloading guns automatically. This was difficult when powder and bullets were separate, although some flintlocks were made self-loading in the early 1600s. The development of the modern cartridge simplified the task, and it is American Samuel Colt who is best remembered for his contribution in this field. From the 1830s, he developed and manufactured reliable revolvers. As the gun's hammer was cocked, a cylinder rotated to bring a fresh round of ammunition in line with the barrel. Repeating rifles using the new type of cartridge included several types produced from the late 1860s by another American, former shirt maker Oliver Winchester, who purchased manufacturing rights from various inventors. Repeaters load a fresh round into the breech when a lever or bolt is operated.

Automatic firearms

Semi-automatic firearms use energy derived from the charge to eject the spent cartridge case and load a fresh round from a magazine. So-called automatic pistols and rifles are mostly of this type. They hold more rounds than a revolver, but are less reliable as the mechanism occasionally becomes jammed.

Fully automatic firearms can be made to fire in bursts. Early designs, dating from the days of the flintlocks, had a row or circle of barrels that were fired in succession by turning a handle. In 1862, American Richard Gatling patented a highly effective multi-barrelled machine gun capable of sustained firing. But it was American inventor Hiram Maxim, former chief engineer of the United States Electric Lighting Company, who established the basic design of the modern machine gun in 1884, with a single-barrelled model operated by the weapon's recoil. Many lightweight machine guns have a mechanism operated by gas from the exploding charge. Some modern automatic weapons can fire more than 1,500 rounds per minute, the ammunition being fed from a belt.

above A London shopkeeper assessing the damage to his premises in 1941, after a bombing raid by the Luftwaffe during the night. The intense air attack, known as the Blitz, took place between September 1940 and May 1941.

Explosives and bombs

Although black powder was used in guns for centuries, it was not without drawbacks. The thick smoke produced when the powder exploded revealed the soldier's position, and deposits had to be frequently removed from the barrel. German chemist Christian Shoenbein developed guncotton in 1845, and this later replaced black powder because, besides being more powerful, it was also a clean, smokeless explosive. Nitroglycerine, first made by Italian chemist Ascanio Sobrero in 1846, was so dangerous to handle that it was of little value until Swedish physicist Alfred Nobel mixed it with a porous earth called kieselguhr to make a form of dynamite, which he patented in 1867. This was ideal for blasting in quarries, its main wartime use being for sabotage.

Grenades filled with black powder were used in warfare from the 1400s, and specially trained soldiers were designated as grenadiers from the 1600s. The first air raid occurred in 1849, when Austrian troops attacked revolting Venetians with bombs attached to hot-air balloons. Most of the fuses burnt far too quickly and exploded the bombs before they had reached their target.

above British tanks advancing towards the Hindenburg Line — the German defences on the Western Front — on 29 September 1918. The location is Bellicourt, France, about 150km north of Paris. The war ended at 11 a.m. on 11 November.

far left Werner von Braun, the 'father of rocket technology'. He developed the V1 and V2 guided rockets. After World War II he worked for the U.S. Army ballistic weapons development group, and then for NASA, where he was part of the team that produced the Saturn rockets that took men to the Moon.

left A V2 rocket, a long-range, supersonic ballistic missile used with devastating effect by the Germans during WWII.

The Italians were the first to use airplanes for bombing, when they flew over Turkey in 1911 and dropped grenades by hand.

This same technique was used by both sides in World War I, but only small bombs could be carried, and these caused little damage to a target unless they made a direct hit. As bomber aircraft became larger, so too did the bombs they carried and, as the high explosive TNT (trinitrotoluene) had become available, aerial bombardment became a terrifying prospect. By World War II, the largest bombs were weighed in tons, rather than pounds, and Britain's 10-ton 'Grand Slams' were the biggest of all. With bombing raids causing so much damage, great efforts were made to shoot down the planes before they reached their targets, and both sides suffered heavy losses in aircraft and crews. Then the Germans perfected techniques for delivering explosives by missile, greatly reducing costs and eliminating the risk to their airmen.

Guided missiles

As early as World War I, the Americans had experimented with pilotless planes with preset controls to guide them towards their targets, and they experimented with radio-controlled missiles in the 1920s. But the Germans became the first to use guided missiles in combat when, in June 1944, they launched the first of their V-1 flying bombs from occupied France. These 7.5-metre-long missiles carried about 900kg of explosive and flew at almost 600 kph, the impulse-jet engine making a low buzzing noise that warned of its approach. The V-2 rocket-powered missile was nearly twice as long as the V-1 and travelled eight times as fast. The Germans first launched it from Holland in September 1944. Being supersonic, the V-2 could not be heard as it approached and was extremely difficult to intercept.

By the time the war with Germany ended in May 1945, the widespread damage inflicted by these weapons, especially on London and Antwerp, showed that missile technology would play an important part in future military confrontations. And the threat from the air was further underlined when, in August 1945, the United States dropped atomic bombs on the Japanese cities Hiroshima and Nagasaki, killing about 130,000 people. This is said to have brought the war with Japan to an end, although some historians feel that the end was already in sight and that the exploding of these new weapons was carried out to demonstrate America's increased military might.

Modern weapons

America's first atomic bombs were developed in a project started in 1940, after German physicist and refugee Albert Einstein had approached President Franklin Roosevelt. Einstein explained that a nuclear fission reaction, in which atomic nuclei are split, could suddenly release an enormous amount of heat energy. The result would be a devastating explosion, far more powerful than had ever before been produced by conventional explosives. The development programme, known by the code name Manhattan Project, resulted in the production of atomic bombs in 1945. The first one, tested in New Mexico in July, had an explosive power equivalent to about 17,000 tonnes of TNT, and its success led to the bombing of Hiroshima and Nagasaki the following month.

Since that time, scientists have developed the far more devastating hydrogen bomb, which uses the process of nuclear fusion, in which heat is released when atomic nuclei are joined. The power of the largest H-bombs is equivalent to tens of millions of tonnes of TNT.

The neutron bomb is a nuclear weapon ideal for a country wishing to take over another's territory, rather than inflict maximum damage. This bomb produces relatively little heat and blast, so it causes limited damage to buildings, but it generates large amounts of radiation to kill personnel.

Biological and chemical weapons are another serious threat to personnel, and the effects on survivors can be long-lasting. In the 1990s, some old soldiers were still suffering discomfort from the effects of breathing chlorine gas released by the Germans during the trench warfare of World War I, some 80 years earlier.

above The crew in the turret of a Chieftain, one of the more heavily armoured tanks of the post-World War II period. Its steel plates are up to 120mm thick, and it weighs about 55 tonnes. In the 1970s, Chieftans replaced the British Army's Centurion tanks.

15

communications

15

Systems of communications have always been essential to everyday life, and ancient civilizations developed various methods of sending simple signals. Many developments that we might think of as recent have their roots in systems invented many centuries ago. A form of telegraph had been established before ways of using electricity had been discovered, and a reliable form of air mail was in use long before balloons and planes took to the skies. Digital signalling sounds like a modern invention, as it is usually associated with computer technology or the latest television transmission techniques. But the term simply means conveying messages by pulses of some kind and, therefore, includes primitive signalling systems, such as drum beats and smoke signals. The lighting of a beacon on a hilltop to warn of an approaching enemy was an early form of a binary (two-state) digital signal; fire meant danger, and no fire meant no danger. At least, there were just these two possibilities when everything was working as intended although, like most communications systems, it could easily fail, and no fire sometimes meant damp wood. Throughout the history of communications, reliability has been of prime importance, and failures have brought many disasters.

Another important factor is the speed of communication. Early warnings of enemy movements have always been vital to governments and military leaders, who have therefore had a major influence on the development of communications systems.

Julius Caesar's method of conveying messages to and from the battlefront was to use relay teams of riders on horseback. A similar system was used in the US by the successful Pony Express mail service, which achieved delivery speeds of more than 300km per day in the early 1860s. The Mongol warrior Genghis Khan became the inventor of the first long-distance airmail postal system when, in the late 1100s, he set up lines of relay stations for homing pigeons across Asia and into Europe.

previous A radio transmitting site in Rio, Brazil. The transmitters of major terrestrial radio stations may be situated many kilometres from the studios, as the aerials need to be on high ground for maximum range.

below An early Morse telegraph receiver. Incoming telegraph signals, transmitted in Morse code, made an electromagnet force a stylus against a moving paper tape. This embossed the dots and dashes along the tape.

Telegraph

In France, Napoleon Bonaparte's desire for a rapid signalling system for the army resulted in Claude Chappe developing the semaphore, or visual telegraph, in the early 1790s. A line of towers, built on high ground and spaced up to 16km apart, was set up between Lille and Paris, a distance of just over 200km. By pulling strings, the operator at a tower could set wooden arms at various angles to signal letters and numbers. At the next tower, the operator used a telescope to observe the signals, noted what was sent and then relayed the message to the next point. This early telegraph worked well, but depended on good visibility.

Electric Telegraph

The sparks and shocks produced by electrical friction machines had been amusing people since the 1660s, but it was difficult to put frictional electricity to practical use. Not until Alessandro Volta's invention of the electric battery in 1800 did a steady and safe supply of electricity become available for experimenters. This led Danish physics professor Hans

left French authorities inspecting one of Claude Chappe's visual telegraph stations in the early 1790s. These were set up to provide a long-distance signalling system for the French army.

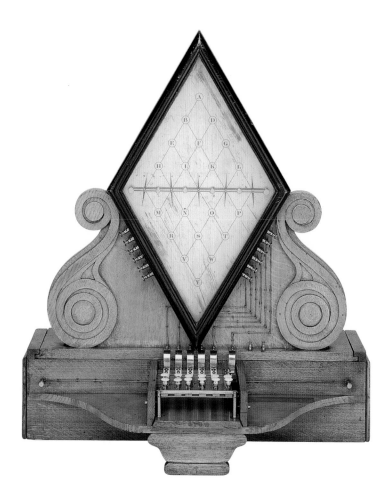

left A five–needle electric telegraph set, the invention of Wheatstone and Cooke in the 1830s. Incoming signals energised electromagnets, and these deflected pairs of magnetic needles, which pointed to letters on the board.

Christian Oersted to discover electromagnetism in 1819. He found that a wire carrying an electric current had a magnetic effect and would deflect the needle of a compass. This, in turn, led to the invention of the electric telegraph, and the start of the modern era of telecommunications.

In 1837, British scientists Charles Wheatstone and William Cooke invented an electric telegraph system. The principle was simple: a current flowing down a long wire would deflect a magnetic needle at the other end. The Wheatstone and Cooke telegraph used several wires and needles to to make a group of needles point to letters of the alphabet.

By this time, an electric current could do much more than merely deflect a needle. Work by Dominique Arago and André Ampère had led English physicist William Sturgeon to invent the practical electromagnet in the early 1820s. Sturgeon greatly increased the magnetic effect of a current by winding many turns of wire on an iron former. Parts of mechanisms could be moved by such electromagnets and, therefore, controlled from a distance by applying an electric current.

American Samual Morse, working with Alfred Vail, used the electromagnet in his telegraph system, also invented in 1837. Short and long pulses of electricity, representing the dots and dashes of his code for letters and numbers, caused an electromagnet to press a stylus onto a moving paper tape, producing an embossed record of the signals. These were then translated back into sentences.

Many other kinds of telegraph system were to follow. Some systems transmitted the dots and dashes automatically when a letter was selected, while others needed an operator to tap out the code on a switch called a Morse key. The pulses could be automatically printed in ink, or a skilled operator could translate them into words simply by listening to the clicks made by a device called a sounder. Eventually, messages could be tapped out on a typewriter-style keyboard and automatically printed at the receiving end, as in teletypewriter, or telex machines.

From the start, the ability to send messages so rapidly by telegraph proved of immense value, especially in combatting crime. The world's first public telegraph service had been established in England in 1843 along a 32km stretch of the Great Western Railway line running westward to Slough from the London terminal at Paddington. In 1845, a chemist called John Tawell took the train to Slough, where he murdered his mistress to end her blackmailing. A neighbour had seen Tawell leaving the woman's house, so the local police sent a telegram to their colleagues in London. The surprised Tawell was arrested as he disembarked at Paddington, and he was later found guilty and hanged in public.

Although types of needle telegraph were still in limited use in England for sending railway signalling messages as late as the 1940s, the American system had proved to be more practical. In 1844, Samual Morse successfully transmitted a message over 60km wires between Baltimore, Maryland, and Washington D.C., thus launching the first public telegraph service in the USA. So great was the demand for this new service that, within just six years, 50 companies were operating telegraph systems in the United States.

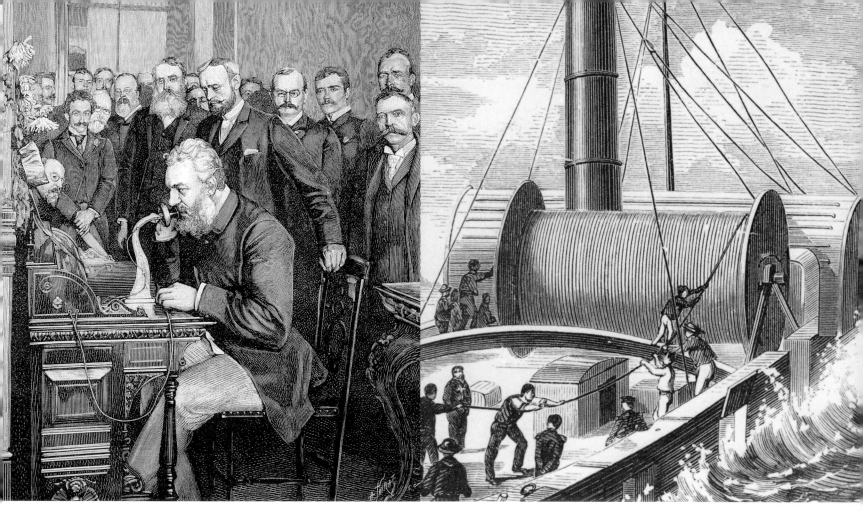

above Scottish-born American inventor Alexander Graham Bell invented the telephone in 1876. The instrument soon incorporated improvements by others. Bell is seen here opening the New York–Chicago telephone service in 1892.

above right Engineers aboard the steamship *Blazer* laying the first successful telegraph cable across the English Channel in 1851. The cable was laid from Dover to Calais, a distance of about 34km.

In 1861, the Western Union Telegraph Company established the first line to link the east and west coasts of the USA. By this time, a cable had already been laid across the Atlantic, but it was faulty. A successful transatlantic telegraph service was eventually established in 1866, and people no longer had to wait weeks for their messages to go by road, rail and sea, and then for the reply to return in the same way. Now that we take instant communications for granted, it is easy to forget just how amazing it must have been in those days for someone to receive a reply from friends across the sea so soon after sending them a message.

However, something even more amazing was just around the corner. For the telephone was soon to allow people to talk to each other by wire. Not surprisingly, many simply refused to believe it could be possible!

Telephone

Alexander Graham Bell was an inventor with an interest in telegraph systems. Born in Scotland in the mid-1800s, Bell emigrated to Canada in 1870 and, the following year, settled in Boston, Massachusetts, and became an American citizen. Bell's father, Alexander Melville, had lectured on elocution at Edinburgh University and, by 1881, was in Washington D.C., teaching deaf-mutes how to communicate with others. His system, called visible speech, involved showing his students exactly how speech sounds were made and how the mouth moved when forming various syllables. This led the lecturer's inventive son to think about ways of making an electric current vary in the same way that our speech organs made the air pressure vary. For if he could do this, then he would be able to transmit speech signals along telegraph wires. Of course, he would also have to find a way of turning the speech signals back into sounds again at the other end.

In 1831, English scientist Michael Faraday had discovered the effect known as electromagnetic induction. Relative movement between a magnet and a coil of wire would induce a voltage in the coil. In other words, movement could be used to make electricity. Bell intended to use this effect in a form of telegraph system he was developing.

In 1875, Bell was trying to find a way of sending several telegraph messages simultaneously over the same wires. Instead of transmitting pulses of steady current from a battery, he thought of generating a varying signal by plucking a metal strip mounted near a magnet. The resulting vibrations would induce a voltage, fluctuating at the same rate, or frequency, in a nearby coil of wire. This voltage would make a current flow along a wire and through an electromagnet at the other end. The rapidly fluctuating magnetic field produced would make an identical metal strip vibrate in resonance with the first and produce a similar sound. Strips of other lengths would hardly vibrate at all. Electric signals of different frequencies, produced by vibrating strips of different lengths, could therefore be sent along the same wires and separated at the other end using different length strips. What Bell had invented was a form of

below Early telephone exchanges employed large numbers of operators, as each call had to be connected manually. Automatic mechanical switches were introduced from 1889. Computers now connect most calls.

mechanical tuning, similar to the electronic tuning techniques we now used to separate radio stations transmitting on different frequencies.

With the idea of sending speech signals by wire ever on his mind, it was not long before Bell found a way of adapting his telegraph transmitter to send signals corresponding to sounds made by the human voice. Success came in one of those moments that has become immortalized by a simple sentence. 'Mr Watson, come here, I want you!', said Bell, summoning his assistant from a nearby room. Watson appeared, having clearly heard Bell's voice in the receiver. The year was 1876, and Bell had invented the first practical telephone.

Instead of using a set of metal strips, Bell's telephone transmitter had a diaphragm of thin iron, which vibrated when sound waves struck it. This caused variations in the field produced by a nearby magnet, and these variations appeared as a varying voltage across a coil of wire. In other words, the transmitter was an electrical generator whose voltage varied according to the patterns of sound waves. The varying voltage, or speech signal, was sent along a pair of wires to a similar device, which could also act as a receiver, or reproducing instrument. In this, the varying voltage passing through the coil gave rise to a varying magnetic field, and this caused the iron diaphragm to vibrate and reproduce the original sounds.

Bell's telephone worked well over short distances, but the signals were too weak for long-distant communications as they were generated entirely by tiny sound vibrations. The electrical resistance of long connecting wires reduced the signals so much that the sounds became inaudible at the far end of a long line.

Within two years, other inventors had solved the problem. Vibrations of the diaphragm varied the pressure on a mass of carbon particles, causing their electrical resistance to vary too. A current from a battery flowed through the particles, and its strength varied as the resistance changed. The result was a sound signal similar to that produced by Bell's transmitter, but the use of a battery made it many times stronger.

Credit for the invention of the carbon transmitter, or microphone, must go to several people. Emile Berliner had the idea of using the sound waves to vary the pressure on a steel contact carrying a current. Thomas Alvar Edison got better results using carbon, instead of steel, and the Reverend Henry Hunnings was the first to use carbon granules, which provided numerous contacts for the current to pass through and gave much improved results. Anthony White further improved the carbon transmitter in 1890, and the resulting instrument, although very simple in design, proved good enough to remain in use for over a century.

One disadvantage of the carbon microphone is that the granules sometimes become clogged together, causing the transmitted sounds to be weak and distorted, though this can be overcome by giving the telephone handset a sharp blow. Although many telephones with carbon microphones are still in use, electromagnetic types have made a comeback in recent years. Miniature electronic amplifiers inside the instrument strengthen the weak signals from the microphone to the level obtained from a carbon type, so it can be heard at a reasonable level and with little distortion.

above The miniaturisation of components mean that it is now possible to use a mobile phone or palmtop computer to access the internet from anywhere in range of a network of transmitters.

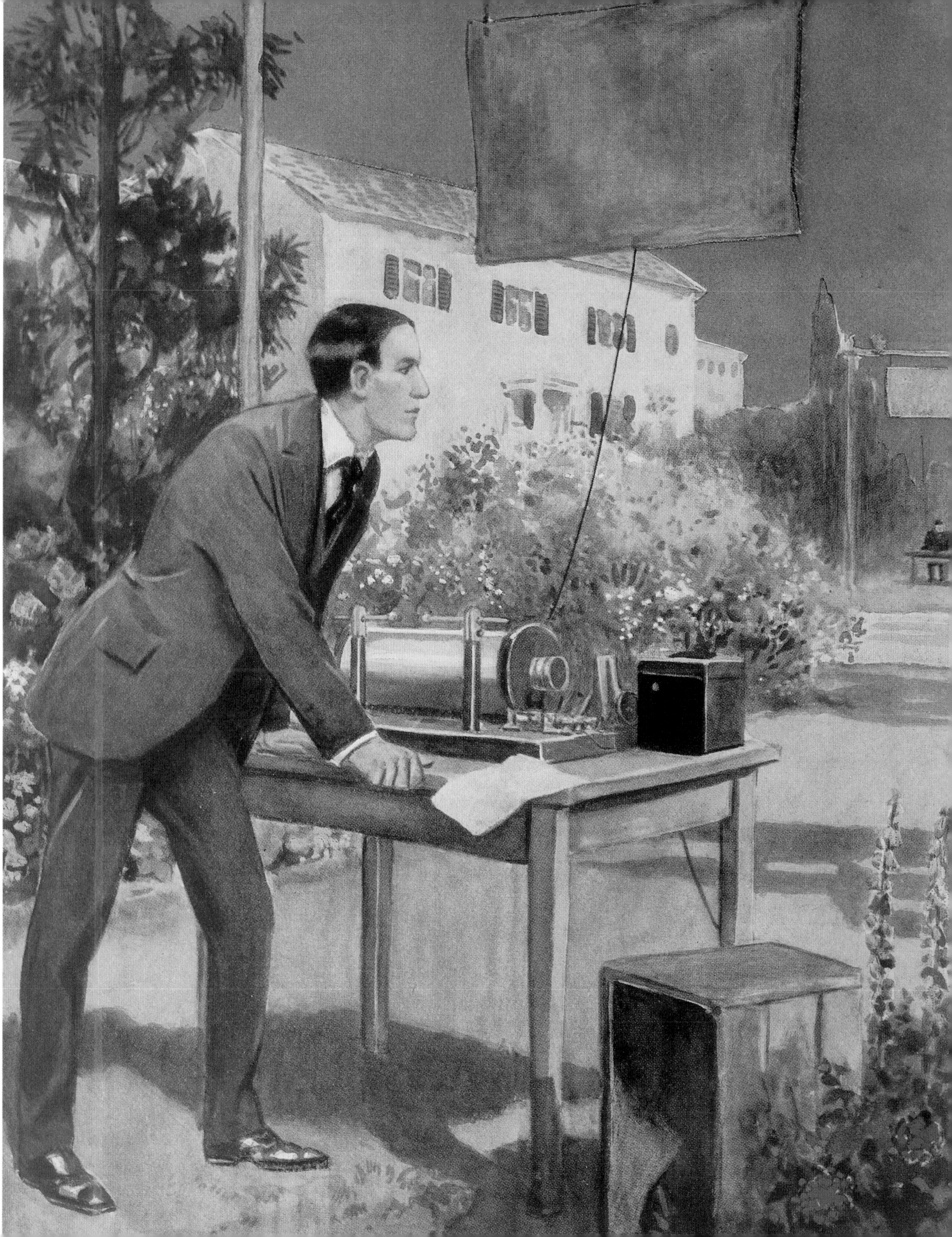

Wireless

The development of wireless communications was a truly international effort. The idea that an electric current might be used to produce invisible electromagnetic waves was made by Scottish physicist James Clerk Maxwell in 1864. Maxwell's idea was shown to be true in 1887 when, in Germany, Heinrich Hertz transmitted radio waves from a simple transmitter. This was before the development of devices that we now think of as 'electronic', and the transmitter was little more than a means of producing a high voltage and discharging it as a spark across a gap between the ends of two metal rods. Hertz's receiver was even simpler. He attached two small metal spheres to the ends of a thick copper wire, just over two metres in length, and bent it to form a circle, leaving a small gap between the spheres. When Hertz switched on his transmitter and placed the receiver nearby, a spark appeared in the gap. The receiver had picked up radio waves from the transmitter and changed them back into electricity, which produced the spark. With this crude apparatus, Hertz was not able to detect his transmission beyond a distance of about 1.5 metres, but he had begun the process of putting Maxwell's theory to practical use.

In France, Edouard Branley devised a more sensitive receiver in 1890. Instead of using the current produced by the received signal to form a spark, Branley passed it through a device that came to be known as a coherer. This contained a mass of loosely packed iron filings, which did not normally conduct electricity very well. But, when a small current passed through them, they clung together to form a much better conductor. This allowed a much stronger current, supplied by a battery, to operate an indicator, such as a meter or an electric bell. Using this detector, Branley could detect radio signals several metres away from the transmitter. Although relatively sensitive, the coherer had a major drawback; after receiving a signal, it had to be tapped to separate the filings before it could be used again.

In England, Oliver Lodge conducted similar experiments. In 1894, he improved the coherer, and sent a message in Morse code by switching his transmitter on and off to produce bursts of radio waves. His receiver picked up these signals from a distance of several hundred metres. Thus began the era of wireless telegraphy – the transmission of coded messages by radio.

Much more work needed to be done before wireless telegraphy could be of practical use, and this was to be started in that same year by a young and enthusiastic Italian. Twenty-year-old Guglielmo Marconi had studied physics at technical school, and had read about the early experiments in wireless communications. He was keen to carry out some experimental work of his own, and started by repeating Lodge's experiments. Then he set about the task of increasing the effective range of transmission by building a more powerful transmitter based on the design Hertz had used. Marconi found that he could greatly increase the strength of the radiated signals if, instead of using two rods to transmit the signals, he used wires to connect the transmitter to two metal plates –

Guglielmo Marconi (1874-1937)

Italian inventor Guglielmo Marconi developed the first practical wireless telegraphy equipment in the 1890s. This led to radio telephony — the transmission of speech messages by wireless, and then to radio and television broadcasting.

Marconi failed the entrance examination for the university in his home town of Bologna, and instead attended technical college at Livorno, on the north-west coast of Italy. He studied science and had a particular interest in electricity and magnetism, and the production of radio waves. In 1894, Marconi began a series of experiments at his father's estate in Bologna (shown left). Using various kinds of transmitting and receiving equipment, he managed to extend the range of his wireless signalling system from just a few metres to over two kilometres. Marconi told the Italian government of his achievement, but they expressed no interest in the project.

In 1896, the young inventor left for England, where he found the support he needed. He continued his experiments and developed telegraphy equipment for communicating with ships. His greatest success came in 1901, when his equipment transmitted a signal across the Atlantic, from Poldhu, in Cornwall, England, to St John's, in Newfoundland, now a province of Canada. Marconi later developed short-wave and microwave communications systems

In 1909, Marconi shared the Nobel Prize for physics, and he later received many other awards, including several honorary degrees.

one high in the air, and the other buried in the ground. He used similar aerial and earth connections at the receiver, which contained his own improved version of the coherer designed by Lodge.

Marconi's first transmissions did not travel far, but he steadily improved his system and increased the range from a few metres to a few hundred metres and, by early 1896, to nearly 2.5km. Realising the importance of his achievements, Marconi approached the Italian authorities, feeling sure they would be sufficiently interested in his work to provide financial backing for further research. But, like so many other inventors throughout history, he was turned down by those who had most to gain. They simply would not be convinced that Marconi's equipment was anything more than an interesting novelty.

The Italian was not one to be put off by such a response and soon left for England, where he approached Sir William Preece, chief engineer of the Post Office. Preece shared Marconi's enthusiasm for the new technology and agreed to assist with his experiments. Marconi filed his first English patent in June and carried out experiments aimed at increasing the range still further. One technique was to use a balloon to carry the aerial wire to a great height. On Salisbury Plain, Wiltshire, he achieved a transmission range of 6.4km. He then went to the west country, where Preece had been experimenting with wireless equipment. In 1897, Marconi successfully sent a message across the water to Flatholme Island, in the Bristol Channel, a distance of about 14km.

Preece gave lectures on Marconi's work, and the resulting publicity attracted the attention of the Italian Government. As a result, Marconi was invited back to his homeland, where he demonstrated his system by establishing communications with naval vessels, some at distances of more than 18km. Yet still there was opposition to the idea of having permanent installations of wireless equipment on board ships.

Marconi continued his work in England and increased the range to 29km in 1898, when he transmitted a message from Poole, on the south coast, to Alum Bay, on the Isle of Wight.

Tuning

Early wireless transmissions consisted of bursts of what, today, we would call interference. Spark transmitters radiated signals that covered a wide range of frequencies. Such transmissions would be detectable almost anywhere on the dial of a modern radio receiver and, if two transmissions were made at the same time, their signals would be superimposed. Clearly, if wireless communication was to become widespread, some way had to be found of separating the signals from transmitters. Oliver Lodge had found the answer in 1897, when he introduced the principle of tuning. This technique, which he called syntony, used a coil of wire and a condenser (capacitor) to confine the signals of a transmitter to a selected range of frequencies. Transmitters could be set to different frequencies, and a similar tuning circuit in a receiver would allow the selection of any signal without interference from the others.

Marconi realised the importance of Lodge's work and, in 1898, installed tuning circuits in his own equipment. With two transmitters set to

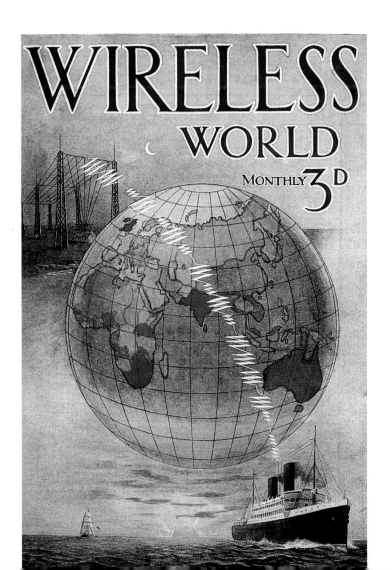

different frequencies, he was able to send two messages simultaneously, and pick them up separately in receivers tuned to the appropriate frequencies. This experiment was carried out on the south coast of England over a distance of nearly 50km.

With such a range, Marconi realised that he would be able to link England with the European mainland. This he achieved in 1899, with transmissions over the 50km between South Foreland, on the English southeast coast, and Wimereux, France. Later, British naval vessels used Marconi's equipment to achieve ranges of well over 100km. But such important achievements did not attract as much attention as they deserved. The general public started to take an interest only when wireless began affecting things that were important in their own lives. In September of that year, Marconi got the publicity he sought when ships transmitted progress reports on the America's Cup yacht race back to newspapers in New York City and, shortly afterwards, he was able to establish the American Marconi Company. In 1900, his British company, The Wireless Telegraph and Signal Company, became Marconi's Wireless Telegraph Company, and he also established the Marconi International Marine Communication Company.

Bridging the Atlantic

Having bridged the English Channel and achieved much greater ranges between ships, Marconi set out to tackle a far more ambitious project. His aim was to send messages across the Atlantic. Some prominent scientists were sceptical, and thought that wireless telegraphy was already approaching its limits. For radio waves, like light, were a form of electro-magnetic radiation and seemed to travel in straight lines. So what was going to make Marconi's transmissions bend so far around the curvature of the Earth? Marconi did not know the answer, but he had evidence that wireless waves did, somehow, reach beyond the horizon, and was fairly confident that he would conquer the Atlantic.

In December 1901, Marconi announced to the world that, at St John's, Newfoundland, he had received a signal from Poldhu, in Cornwall, England – more than 3,000km away. The experiment was carried out under difficult conditions, Marconi using a kite to raise the aerial wire as high as possible, and the brief Morse signal he eventually received was weak. But this proved that signals could somehow travel around the curvature of the Earth, and it marked the beginning of long-distance wireless telegraphy. We now know that radio waves can travel over long distances by bouncing from the ionosphere – a layer of charged particles high above the Earth.

Radio Telephony

In the back of many minds was the thought that, as telephone signals could be sent over telegraph wires, then perhaps it would be possible to send them over a wireless system too. For wireless telephony to work, a telephone transmitter, or microphone, had to pick up sounds and vary the transmitted signal in some way, and the variations had to be changed back into sounds in the receiver. Headphones, consisting of a pair of

opposite The cover of a 1915 edition of *Wireless World*, a leading publication in the field of radio communications. Wireless had become an important means of communication and had helped to save many lives at sea.

below The arrest in 1910 of Hawley Harvey Crippen and his lover Ethel Le Neve (disguised as a boy). For the first time, a wireless message had helped to catch a criminal. The captain of the *Montrose* had alerted police that the wanted couple were aboard. Crippen was found guilty and hanged for murdering his wife.

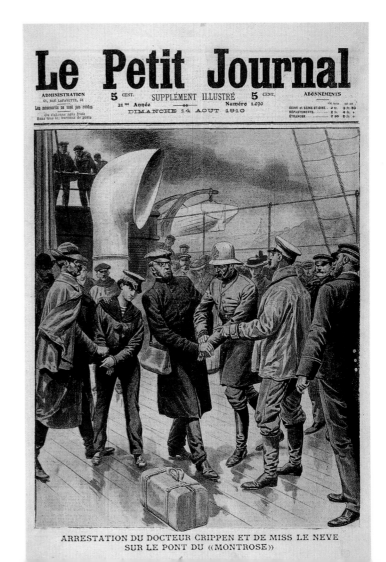

ARRESTATION DU DOCTEUR CRIPPEN ET DE MISS LE NEVE
SUR LE PONT DU «MONTROSE»

devices based on telephone earpiece design, enabled radio operators to listen to the Morse telegraphy signals that they received. The signals from spark transmitters consisted of irregular bursts of energy and gave rise to an irritating noise in the headphones. Clearly, this basic signal would have to be silenced or, at least, subdued if speech was to be somehow superimposed on it. And there was also the question of how to use a microphone to control the transmitted signal.

In 1899, an Englishman called William Duddell suggested using an electric arc in a transmitter instead of a series of sparks. Three years later, a Dane called Valdemar Poulson put this idea into practice. The arc, powered by direct current, gave rise to a continuous stream of radio waves and provided a better basic signal on which the speech could be superimposed. This was done by connecting a carbon microphone in the supply to the arc so that, when the operator spoke into the microphone, the strength of the arc varied, and so did the strength of the radiated radio waves. As the radio waves were thus made to carry superimposed sound signals, the original stream of radio waves eventually became known as the carrier. The process of superimposing sound signals on the carrier was called modulation, and the resulting signals were called modulated waves. Others experimented with alternative methods of producing radio waves, the simplest being the use of a high-frequency electricity generator, which produced an almost pure signal and provided a silent background for the speech signals.

In the United States, R A Fessenden was one of several Americans interested in speech transmission by wireless. At Pittsburgh University, Virginia, he had successfully sent spoken messages over short distances and, like other experimenters, he steadily increased the range of his transmissions. Eventually, on Christmas Eve, 1906, Fessenden made history by transmitting a poetry reading and a short violin recital. By that time, his transmitter had a range of hundreds of kilometres, and wireless equipment was becoming common on ships. Many wireless operators listening for Morse telegraphy signals were astonished to hear instead

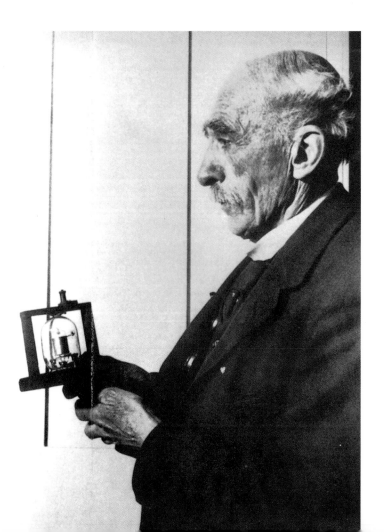

above British inventor of the thermionic valve, or vacuum tube, Sir John Ambrose Fleming. This valve was a diode, which passed current in one direction only. Its invention in 1904 led Lee De Forest to invent the triode amplifying valve two years later.

Fessenden's short programme of entertainment. Although this transmission did not mark any great technical advance, it was the first programme to be broadcast by wireless, and some people began to realise that wireless technology promised much more than telegraphy and telephony. For a single transmitter could cover a large area and provide the general public with entertainment too. However, the thought that members of the public might have equipment that enabled them to listen in to private messages tended to discourage the authorities from wanting to authorise general broadcasting systems, so wireless continued for some time to be used mainly for messages.

The Electronic Age

German scientist Karl Ferdinand Braun discovered a strange phenomenon in 1874. He found that some pairs of different conductors, when placed in light contact, would allow an electric current to flow in one direction, but would prevent much flow in the other direction. An assembly of two such materials became known as a rectifier, or diode, and was an important item in early wireless receivers. For it was the main component used in separating sound signals from the carrier waves. In a receiver, carrier waves produced an electrical signal that alternated, or changed direction, very quickly. The changes in strength that corresponded to the sound signal could not be heard simply by listening to the carrier on headphones because, before the effect of a positive pulse of current could be detected, a following negative pulse would produce a cancelling effect. A rectifier cut out one half of the incoming signal, eliminating this cancelling effect, and allowing the sound signal to be reconstructed.

A popular type of rectifier consisted of a crystal of galena (lead sulphide), mounted in a brass holder, with a wire above it. The wire, known as the cat's whisker, had to be adjusted so that it just made contact with a sensitive spot on the crystal. Sounds would then be heard in the headphones of the receiver, which became known as a crystal set.

The sound quality was remarkably good, but the crystal set could not produce much volume because it simply reproduced as sound some of the electrical energy picked up by its long wire aerial. A crude way to amplify the sounds was to pick them up using a battery-powered carbon microphone connected to one or more sets of headphones, and others simply placed headphones in the bottom of a bowl to provide a little acoustic amplification.

Thomas Alva Edison had noticed a strange blackening around the positive end of the filament inside an electric light bulb powered by direct (one-way) current. It was evidence that some unexplained process was taking place in the bulb, but Edison never discovered what it was. If he had, he might have gone on to add the vacuum tube to his already long list of other inventions. But it was left to British electrical engineering professor John Ambrose Fleming to explain the phenomenon. In 1904, he found that negatively charged particles called electrons left the hot carbon filament and were attracted back to bombard its positive end. To investigate further, Fleming introduced a separate metal electrode, called

Lee De Forest (1873-1961)

American physicist Lee De Forest invented the first electronic amplifying device — the Audion vacuum tube (valve), later known as the triode. This was one of the most important inventions of all time, because it led to the development of numerous electronic devices.

De Forest studied science at Yale University and left in 1899 with a PhD in physics. His particular interest was in the theory and application of radio waves, or Hertzian waves, as they were then called. He first worked for the Western Electric Company in

Chicago, and there developed wireless receiving and transmitting devices. In 1902, he formed the De Forest Wireless Telegraph Company, and publicised the new technology by giving demonstrations to interested parties.

The company went out of business, but he invented the Audion triode valve in 1906 and formed the De Forest Radio Telephone Company. He developed circuits for high-gain amplification and for signal generation but, because of his poor business sense, De Forest made little money from these extremely important inventions.

an anode, into an evacuated light bulb and found that, when it was positively charged, a stream of electrons, making up an electric current, would flow to it from the filament. He had invented the diode (two electrode) valve which, because it passed current in one direction only, could be used in place of a crystal and cat's whisker for detecting radio signals. Using a diode valve in a wireless receiver avoided the fiddly business of having to adjust a cat's whisker, but had no other advantage, and there was the disadvantage that it required a battery to heat its filament, so crystal sets remained the popular receivers for many years.

American inventor Lee De Forest went one step further than Fleming and, in 1906, produced a device that was to change the world. He introduced a third electrode, called a grid, between the filament and anode of the vacuum tube to make a triode valve. The grid consisted of a wire mesh through which electrons had to pass on their way from the filament to the anode. By altering the electrical charge on the grid, De Forest found that he could control the flow of electrons through it. For example, a high negative charge on the grid would repel the oncoming electrons so that none of them reached the anode. The most important point about the triode was that a small electric signal applied to the grid would cause quite large changes in the current flowing between filament and anode. In other words, the triode could amplify weak signals. This eventually extended the range of every wireless transmitter in existence because, at long distances from transmitters, signals that were previously undetectable could be amplified and heard clearly. And further amplification could make a sound signal strong enough to power a loudspeaker so that everyone in a room could listen together.

De Forest later found that his triode valve was even more versatile than had been anticipated. In 1912, he discovered that the triode could be used in a wireless transmitter to generate an almost pure carrier signal that provided a silent background for the transmitted sounds. When used in this way as a signal generator, the valve and its associated components were referred to as the oscillator. This arrangement was far less cumbersome and more efficient than other generating equipment.

By this time, wireless telegraphy and telephony were widely used, and many enthusiasts experimented with both receivers and transmitters.

When war broke out in 1914, amateurs found themselves banned from experimenting, but the new technology proved vital to the armed forces, and a new generation of enthusiasts was born as the forces used experienced wireless engineers to train technicians for communications systems. Meanwhile, in the USA, progress was being made in extending the range over which speech could be transmitted by wireless. In 1918, the ending of the war meant that restrictions on civilians using wireless equipment could be lifted, but it was not just the enthusiastic amateur who was to benefit. The time had come for wireless technology to be put into the hands of the general public. It was the dawn of the radio age.

Music from Marconi

In 1920, the Marconi Company built a transmitter at Chelmsford, Essex, to continue their own long-distance test transmissions of speech. Some of the engineers could play musical instruments and so, from time to time, they would sit around a microphone and broadcast a short recital. The response was astonishing. They receive encouraging letters from listeners in England and discovered that they had a devoted following in mainland Europe too. News of these transmissions spread, and public demand for domestic wireless sets quickly grew.

In June 1920, the *Daily Mail* sponsored a broadcast concert that was to leave a lasting impression. Australian soprano Nellie Melba, already known throughout the world, sang a selection of operatic works in Italian, French and English, and was heard not only throughout Europe, but in North America too. After this, the establishment of services devoted to broadcasting was inevitable and, in February 1922, the Marconi Company started transmissions from Station MT2 in Writtle, not far from their Chelmsford establishment. By May, they were broadcasting also from station 2LO at Marconi House in London's Strand. Other firms started broadcasting too, and the British Broadcasting Company was formed in October 1922 by a group of wireless equipment manufacturers, including the Marconi Company. The British Broadcasting Company eventually became the British Broadcasting Corporation in 1927, and was destined to become a world leader in broadcasting technology – not just in radio, but in television too.

above A recording suite in a radio station. Radio stations and television studios can both broadcast live and record material for later use. This development has enabled them to increase their output from the original two or three hours to 24 hours a day.

above left German troops using a field radio set during WWII. Although these short-wave transmitter-receivers used several fairly large valves, careful layout of components resulted in a reasonably compact and robust design.

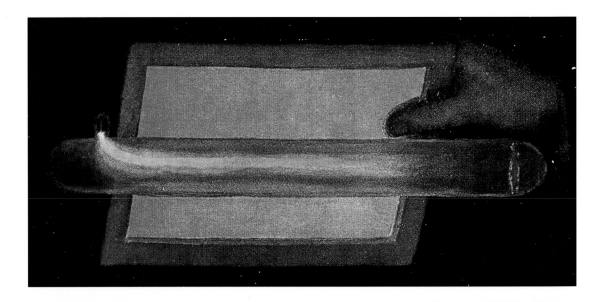

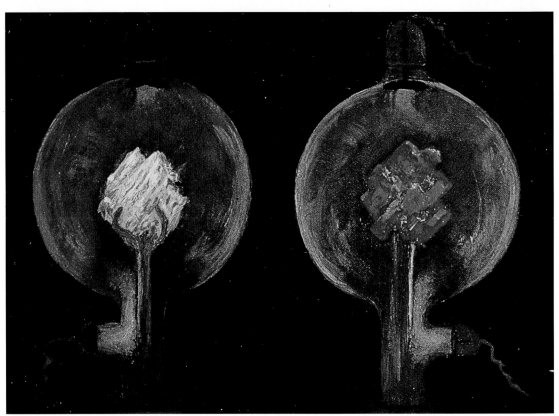

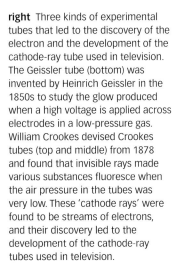

right Three kinds of experimental tubes that led to the discovery of the electron and the development of the cathode-ray tube used in television. The Geissler tube (bottom) was invented by Heinrich Geissler in the 1850s to study the glow produced when a high voltage is applied across electrodes in a low-pressure gas. William Crookes devised Crookes tubes (top and middle) from 1878 and found that invisible rays made various substances fluoresce when the air pressure in the tubes was very low. These 'cathode rays' were found to be streams of electrons, and their discovery led to the development of the cathode-ray tubes used in television.

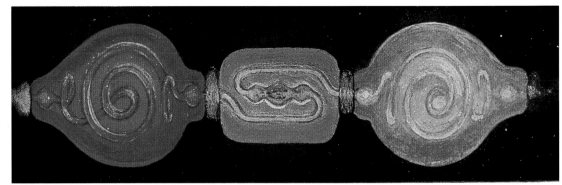

Sir William Crookes (1832-1919)

English scientist William Crookes made important discoveries about cathode rays, and devised vacuum tubes that were the forerunners of the cathode-ray tubes used in television cameras and receivers.

Crookes studied at London's Royal College of Chemistry, and worked as assistant there before becoming superintendant of the meteorological department at Radcliffe Observatory, Oxford, in 1854. The following year, he moved to Chester to teach chemistry at the College of Science. In 1856, Crookes inherited a large sum of money and, no longer having to earn a living, was able to spend the rest of his life carrying out research in scientific matters that interested him.

Crookes founded *Chemical News*, became a Fellow of the Royal Society, and an expert on sewerage. He devised a method for separating silver and gold from their ores, and discovered the element thallium. He also invented the radiometer, an instrument for detecting radiation. But he is best known for his studies of cathode-rays, which in turn led J J Thomson to discover the electron. Crookes was knighted in 1897.

Television

The history of television began with an accidental discovery made as long ago as 1873. Telegraph engineers Willoughby Smith and Louis May noticed that the electric current flowing through some equipment varied mysteriously, yet they could find nothing wrong with the components in the circuit. Eventually, they realised that the cause of the problem was a shaft of sunlight streaming through the window. When the bright light fell on a resistor made of selenium, the current increased slightly, decreasing again when a shadow fell on the component. This phenomenon, now known as a form of photoelectric effect, led to the production of photoelectric cells and, eventually, to the development of television.

The idea of using electricity to see at a distance came in the mid-1870s, more than ten years before Heinrich Hertz was to demonstrate the existence of radio waves. The first designs were for a form of closed-circuit television, with wires connecting the detector and receiver. In 1880, English scientists Ayrton and Perry proposed a system that they called electric vision. Light from a scene would be focused by a camera lens onto an array of small photoelectric cells. These would be connected to an array of small electric light bulbs in such a way that the brightness of the image on each cell would determine the brightness of each bulb. The image on the array of cells would, therefore, be reproduced on the array of bulbs. Even with hundreds of cells and bulbs, the image would have been crude and lacking in detail, but there was nothing wrong with the basic principle. However, the technology of the day simply could not meet the engineers' demands. A photoelectric cell could control only a weak current – far too little to light an electric light bulb – and, at that time, there was no means of amplifying the currents from the cells. So television would have to wait for a while.

Even if the technology had been available to make Ayrton and Perry 's idea of electric vision work, there was a serious problem that would have limited its development. Relatively small arrays of photoelectric cells and bulbs would have been satisfactory for sending images of simple symbols from one place to another but, to show a recognisable scene, many thousands of cells and bulbs would have been needed. This meant that there would have to be thousands of connecting wires between the cells and bulbs, and this would have made the system prohibitively expensive except, perhaps, over very short distances.

Scanning

In 1884, a German called Paul Nipkow came up with a vital improvement. Nipkow overcame the wiring problem by inventing the technique known as scanning. As with many great inventions, the principle was simple. Instead of using an array of cells to measure the brightness of every part of the image at the same time, he would use a single cell to sample tiny elements of the image, one after another. At the receiving end of the system, the picture would be reconstructed using a single bulb to reproduce the brightness of each element of the image in turn. This would all be done so rapidly that, because of the eye's persistence of vision, the display would appear to show, not a series of patches of light, but a complete picture. This was more complex than the system Ayrton and Perry had proposed, but it had the great advantage that, with just one photoelectric cell and one bulb, all that was needed between the sending and receiving equipment was a single pair of wires. And that meant it might be practicable to send pictures along telegraph wires – an astonishing idea for those days, when the telephone was in its very early stages of development.

The vital part of Nipkow's transmitting apparatus was a large rotating disc with a series of small holes near the rim. The image of a scene was made to fall on the disc, which turned rapidly. At any moment, one hole in the disk would be in the image area, allowing a spot of light to pass through the disk and onto a photoelectric cell at the far side. As the disk spun, the hole would pass across the image, allowing the cell to sample the light from a narrow strip of the picture. As soon as one hole had passed across the image, another hole would start to trace another, adjacent path across it. In this way, the equipment scanned the whole of the image, line by line, and the photoelectric cell caused a current to vary according to the brightness of each part of the picture in turn.

The varying current, or vision signal, would be sent along wires to a receiver and displayed on a light bulb, which would flicker as it reproduced the brightness of each picture element in turn. Another disc, like the one in the transmitter, would spin in front of the bulb so that, at any moment, only a single spot of light would be seen, and this would move across the display area, line by line. If the discs in the transmitter and receiver were accurately synchronized, then the brightness variations in the scene would be reproduced in corresponding positions in the receiver display, and the eye would see what appeared to be a complete picture. Nipkow was never able to put his ideas for television into practice because he could not find a way to make the weak vision signal control the brightness of a powerful bulb.

For a while, what we would regard as true television had to wait for new developments in technology. Meanwhile, advances were being made in a related field – fascimile. The first idea for a fax machine had been put forward in 1843 by a Scottish engineer called Alexander Bain. He never perfected his system, which involved a metal stylus making intermittent electrical contact as it scanned in narrow lines across the face of metal type. The pulsating signal thus produced would be sent along telegraph wires to a receiver, where the pulses would be automatically changed back into the patterns of the type characters by a pen scanning across a paper. Although Bain had no success, he had introduced the idea of scanning later adopted by Niplow.

Others soon developed successful mechanical facsimile machines and then, in the early years of the new century, a system much closer to television appeared. German inventor Arthur Korn introduced a machine with a photoelectric cell that scanned the surface of a photograph. The varying current passed by the cell as it slowly scanned the picture was transmitted to a distant receiver, where it was used to control the brightness of a small light bulb as it scanned across photographic film. The

Vladimir Kosma Zworykin (1889-1982)

Russian–born electronics engineer Vladimir Zworykin emigrated to the United States after World War I and developed the technology for which he became known as the father of modern television.

Zworykin studied at St Petersburg Institute of Technology, and then in Paris at the Collège de France. After serving in the Russian army signal corps during World War I, he left the country in 1919 and settled in the USA. From 1920, he worked in Pittsburgh for Westinghouse Electric Corporation, and developed equipment for television. His iconoscope, patented in 1923, was the first television camera tube, and his kinescope, patented in 1924, was the first television picture tube.

When Zworykin demonstrated his television system to the Westinghouse directors, they were not interested enough to go into production. However, Zworykin continued working on his inventions, and demonstrated an improved system to the Radio Corporation of America in 1929. They immediately employed him and, by 1933, had the first all-electronic television system in production.

film was developed to produce an image of the photograph. Korn's invention was important because it was the first successful use of optical scanning, but his receiving equipment could not display live pictures.

Electronics to the rescue

Lee De Forest's 1906 invention of the triode amplifying valve, which had enabled radio technology to advance, also enabled television to become a reality. Another important development was the introduction of more efficient discharge tubes using neon and other gases. Unlike a filament lamp, a neon could be made to flicker extremely rapidly and accurately follow the changing strength of a vision signal – suitably amplified by valves. Television systems using Nipkow discs, amplifying valves, and a neon lamp were developed in France by an engineer called Barthélémy, in the United States by Charles Jenkins, and in Britain by a Scotsman called John Logie Baird.

Many countries like to claim television as their own invention, so many of the British tend to think of Baird as the man who invented the most influential technology of the century. After experiments involving the transmission of silhouettes, Baird eventually demonstrated the transmission by wire of moving pictures containing half-tones – in this case, shades of pink produced by a neon lamp. The picture was made up of only 30 slightly curved lines, running down the tiny and dim image, so it was difficult to make out detail. And the slow repetition rate of about 10 pictures per second meant that the image flickered considerably. Nevertheless, this was the first public demonstration of what may be regarded as true television. It took place in London in 1926, and was important in that it gave those with imagination ideas of what might lie ahead.

People from other countries usually point to their own heroes instead. Some Russians might remind us of Boris Rosing, who had successfully transmitted and received images nearly 20 years earlier. Admittedly, Rosing transmitted only simple patterns, but he did devise a scanning technique in which a spot of light was deflected rapidly across an image by rotating mirrors. This flying spot system of scanning found uses in television long after Baird's televisor had been abandoned. German physicist Karl Braun had invented a cathode-ray tube in 1897 for displaying electrical waveforms, and Rosing suggested that such a tube with a fluorescent screen might be suitable for displaying television pictures, as did Scottish engineer A A Cambell Swinton.

It was Cambell Swinton who, in 1908, first proposed what eventually became the basis of electronic television systems. He described how a television camera could be made using a cathode-ray tube with a light-sensitive screen, scanned by a beam of electrons that was guided by magnetic fields. Cambell Swinton also suggested that the vision signals produced could be reproduced on another special kind of cathode-ray tube. Unfortunately, the imaginative Scot was ahead of his time and the techniques were not yet available for producing all parts of the system he envisaged.

While some engineers and scientists were gradually solving the problems associated with electronic scanning systems, others were

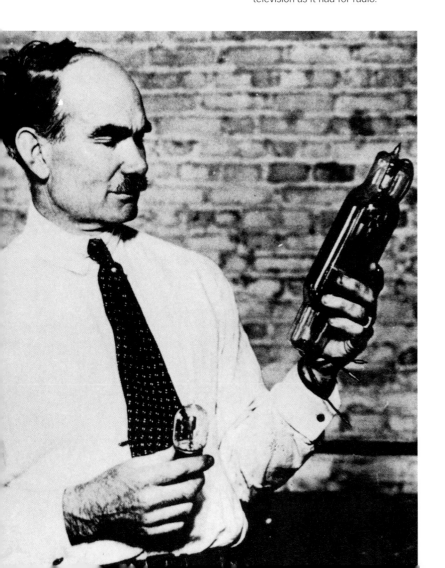

below Lee De Forest's triode valve amplified weak signals and proved as useful in the development of television as it had for radio.

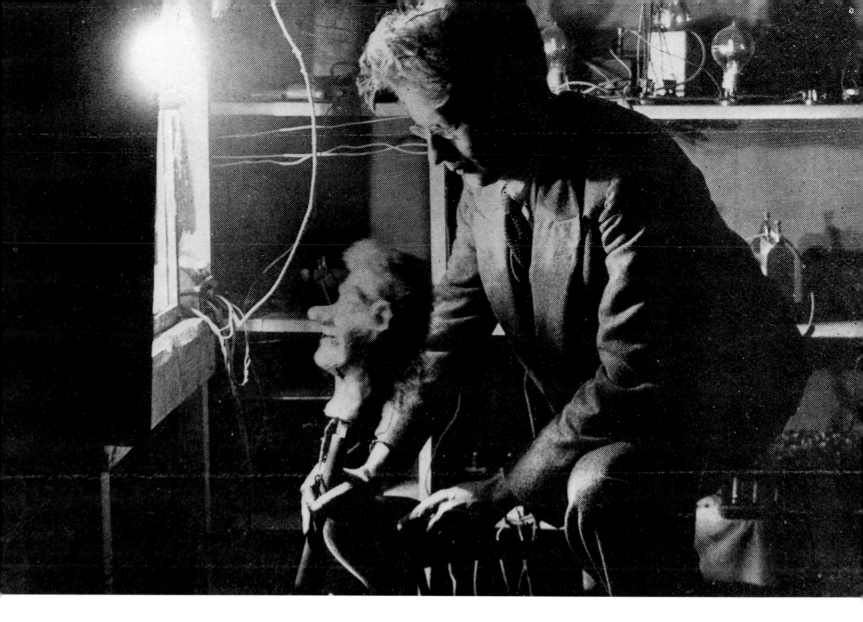

trying to perfect mechanical systems, and these continued to form the basis of most experimental television systems. The first experimental TV broadcasts were made in 1928 by New York's station WGY using a mechanical scanning system and, in London, Baird soon began working with the British Broadcasting Corporation to transmit experimental TV broadcasts on the medium-wave band now used for radio. Around 1930, the limitations of mechanical scanning systems were becoming apparent. To increase the detail in a picture, it would have to be scanned with a larger number of narrower lines, and the scanning would have to be done faster. Also, increasing the number of pictures transmitted each second to reduce flicker required a further increase in scanning speed. There was a limit to the speed at which a Nipkow system could run reliably, and so the BBC decided to experiment with a completely electronic system along the lines suggested all those years ago by Cambell Swinton.

In 1931, a team of physicists was put together to work on the project at the EMI research laboratories, London. The project was directed by Isaac Shoenberg, a Russian who had set up the first radio stations in his home country before settling in London. Four years later, a successful demonstration of the new all-electronic television system to a committee set up by the government led to the BBC getting the go-ahead for

John Logie Baird (1888-1946)

Scotttish inventor John Logie Baird was the inventor who, in 1926, gave the first public demonstration of televised moving pictures.

Baird studied electrical engineering at Glasgow's Royal Technical College and then at the University. The mechanical television system he devised was based on the rotating scanning disc, invented in 1884 by the German Paul Nipkow. The disk, with a series of holes in it, split the image formed by a lens into 30 lines, and a photoelectric cell measured the brightness along them. The resulting vision signal controlled the brightness of a lamp in the receiver, and another Nipkow disk ensured that each element of the picture appeared in the right place. Although his system was used for public broadcasting from 1929, it was replaced in the 1930s by a superior all-electronic system.

above A glass-blower working in a television factory in 1955. The television 'tube' hardly changed in its basic shape until the development of flatter tubes in the 1980s and plasma-filled tubes in the late 1990s.

establishing a British television service. By 1936, the London TV station had been built at Alexandra Palace, London, and the BBC began transmissions to establish the world's first regular television service.

At first, the BBC used both a Baird mechanical system and the EMI electronic system so that they could compare performances. For the electronic scanning system was relatively new technology, while Baird's setup was well tried and tested. However, before long, the new equipment had proved so superior that the Baird system was scrapped. The 405-line high-definition system devised by Shoenberg gave much sharper pictures than Baird's 240-line equipment, and worked so well that it was retained until 1964, when Britain adopted a 625-line standard.

In 1931, just as Shoenberg and his team at EMI started their work in London on an all-electronic television system, the Radio Corporation of America introduced a receiver containing a cathode-ray tube developed by the Russian Vladimir Zworykin and based on a design called the kinescope, which he had patented in 1924. Zworykin had joined RCA as director of electronic research and, in 1933, added an electronic camera to give RCA their own all-electronic television system, three years before the BBC. Zworykin's camera used a cathode-ray tube based on his own iconoscope design, which he had patented ten years earlier.

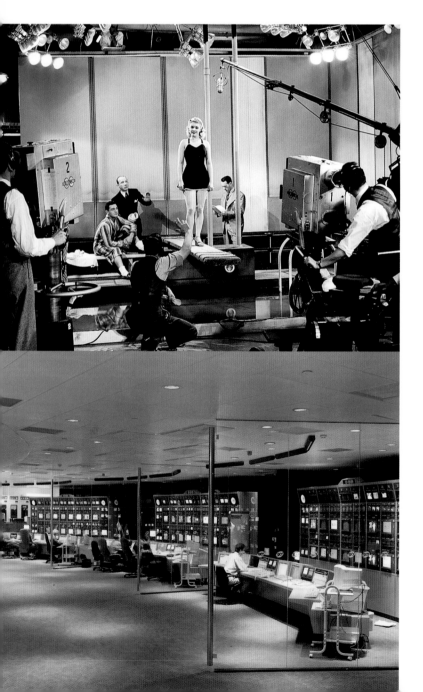

below A television studio scene in the early 1940s. The basic techniques have changed very little since those days, although recordings are now made on tape, instead of film, and colour systems have replaced black-and-white television.

bottom BSkyB's multichannel digital playout centre. Both satellite and cable systems have given people a much wider choice of viewing than could be provided by conventional terrestrial transmitters.

Colour systems

So far, we have looked only at the development of monochrome systems, but colour systems were being considered as early as 1904. In England, Baird acquired another claim to fame in 1928, when he gave the first practical demonstration of a colour television system – mechanical, of course. Baird used a Nipkow disc with three sets of holes, and red, green and blue filters to separate the colour components of the original image. In the receiving equipment, different coloured gas-discharge lamps displayed separate images, which appeared to combine to form a full-colour picture. Meanwhile, others were adopting different approaches, and Zworykin was developing an electronic colour system that he had patented three years earlier.

One problem with colour television was that there were three colour signals, corresponding to the red, green and blue components of the picture. At first, it was assumed that these would be sent to the receiving equipment via three separate channels – cables or radio transmissions. This changed in 1929, when American Frank Gray, working for Bell Telephone Laboratories, worked out a way of sending multiple signals over a single channel.

Another problem took longer to resolve. It was clear that equipment to receive colour pictures was going to be very expensive, and it seemed likely that many people would have to be content with watching in monochrome – neon pink on mechanical systems and, when cathode-ray tubes were introduced, black-and-white. So it was essential for the signals to be transmitted in such a way that every colour in a picture would be represented by an appropriate brightness level on the screen of a monochrome receiver.

The person who did most to solve this problem of compatibility was Frenchman Georges Valensi. In 1938, he described a system for combining the three primary colour signals so that they could be displayed on unmodified monochrome receivers, as well as on colour sets. Today's colour transmission systems are based on modifications of Valensi's techniques. Signals corresponding to the three primary colour components in the image are combined in appropriate proportions to form a luminance, or brightness signal, like that of a monochrome picture. This is transmitted together with a single chrominance signal containing all the colour information. The chrominance signal is in a form that monochrome receivers cannot detect, so they simply display the luminance signal in black-and-white. Colour receivers have additional circuits for detecting and separating the chrominance signal and deriving from it the three primary colour signals. These are used to form a full-colour picture, usually on the screen of a special cathode-ray tube or on a flat liquid-crystal display, although sometimes the picture is thrown onto a large movie screen by separate red, green and blue projectors.

After years of test transmissions and trials, regular colour television broadcasting began in 1954, when the United States adopted a system proposed by their National Television Systems Committee. Japan followed America's example and adopted the NTSC system for their own colour service, which started in 1960. European countries were divided over their

preferences for colour TV systems and, in 1967, Britain and West Germany opted for a modified form of NTSC called the PAL system, which had been developed in Germany by Telefunken, whereas France and the USSR used another variation known as SECAM. A further complication was the use of different numbers of lines per picture, and different numbers of pictures per second.

Modern standards

Today, the European line standard is 625 lines, with 25 pictures per second. Each picture is transmitted in two steps by scanning the odd and even lines alternately. This presents the viewer with 50 images per second from only 25 pictures. The alternate scans are called the odd and even fields and, because of the way the images they form fit together, the technique is called interlaced scanning. The resulting doubling of the repetition rate makes flicker almost undetectable.

This technique – one of Shoenberg's innovations – is used in the American system too, where the standard is 525 lines and 30 complete pictures per second. All other countries now use either the European or American picture standard. Advances in electronics have made the conversion of signals from one line standard to another, and from one colour system to another, a relatively simple matter, so programmes from one country can easily be shown elsewhere – highly convenient in an age when communications satellites allow signals to be beamed across the world in a fraction of a second.

above Communications satellites provide telephone, radio and television links across the world. Many satellites orbit the Equator and move in time with the Earth's spin. These satellites appear to hover in fixed positions, and are described as geostationary. This arrangement is convenient for television broadcasting because viewers can pick up the signals using a simple dish-shaped aerial, fixed in position.

digital
computers

Computers make use of ideas that are centuries old. As with television, it was a long time before technology caught up and enabled the ideas of inspired inventors to become reality.

Today's electronic digital computers can do many things, but these all boil down to processes involving counting, calculating and storing numbers. In prehistoric times, people counted and performed simple calculations on their fingers. A permanent record of a number could be represented by marks on a wall, or pebbles in a container, and sometimes pebbles were used to do the counting and calculating too. In fact, our word calculate comes from calculus, the Latin for pebble.

Around 3000 BC, the ancient Egyptians developed a system of counting in tens, based on the technique of counting on the fingers and, in Mesopotamia, a simple calculating device appeared. Pebbles, placed in a series of grooves in a wooden board, were slid along to record numbers and perform calculations. The grooved board was the first form of abacus, more well known in the bead-frame form as used in ancient Greece, Rome and China, and still used in some parts of the far East today. This ancient device has survived because its basic structure made it difficult to develop further. On the other hand, later calculators incorporating turning wheels were to provide enormous possibilities. In fact, the basic principles by which modern electronic computers operate were conceived long ago in the era of these mechanical calculators.

In 1642, at the age of 19, Blaise Pascal designed a new kind of mechanical calculator for his father, a customs officer in Rouen, France. Pascal, destined to become a leading mathematician, philosopher and physicist, used a series of toothed wheels, each inscribed with the numbers 0 to 9. Moving the wheels to add or subtract caused the numbers seen through a viewing window to change and display the answer. Other inventors improved on Pascal's design, notably German mathematician Gottfried Leibnitz who, in 1671, enabled the calculator to multiply by carrying out repeated additions of the same number. However, because of difficulties in making sufficiently accurate gear wheels, it was not until the 1800s that mechanical calculators became reliable enough to generate general interest. Meanwhile, pen and paper remained the main tools of mathematicians engaged in calculating navigation tables and other numerical data, such as logarithms.

previous Part of an IBM computer made in 1971. This machine, which had a memory of 2 megabytes, cost £2,500,000. Today, desktop computers of much greater power are thrown away because they have become outdated.

right French scientist, mathematician and philosopher Blaise Pascal with his mechanical calculator of 1642. Such devices established some of the principles later used in electronic calculators and computers.

Charles Babbage (1791-1871)

Long before the age of electronics, English mathematician Charles Babbage established the basic principles of automatic digital computers when he designed mechanical calculators.

Babbage first had the idea for the mechanical calculator he called the difference engine in 1812, while studying mathematics at Cambridge University, England. But, by the early 1830s, he had built only a simplified model of this machine, and he abandoned its development in order to embark on a more ambitious project. He designed a calculator, called the analytical engine, that used punched cards to hold both the data and a set of instructions detailing the calculations to be performed. He had introduced the idea of data and program storage, concepts that were later to be used in electronic digital computers. The complex parts needed for this machine were impossible to make with sufficient precision in Babbage's time, so this project was abandoned too. But, because of the important principles Babbage introduced, he is sometimes called the father of the digital computer.

Difference engine

Because human calculators are bound to make mistakes, a new system of devising and checking mathematical tables was introduced in France. First of all, the calculations were broken down into several simple stages that even relatively unskilled people could carry out. Then the results of calculations were entered in columns, and the differences between successive results were entered in an adjacent column. This process was repeated to produce further columns of difference figures and eventually resulted in a column in which all the numbers should have been the same. The existence of an error in the calculations was therefore clearly obvious on inspection of the final column of differences.

This new approach intrigued Charles Babbage, an English banker's son who had entered Cambridge University in 1811 to study mathematics. Babbage realized that, as all columns following the original series of results were obtained by subtraction, it was possible to extend the final column of identical numbers and work back through the differences columns, using addition, to derive further figures in the required series of numbers. Thus it would be possible to extend the table indefinitely by

using simple arithmetic, and Babbage proposed doing this work on a machine that was to be called the difference engine. Babbage also intended using the machine to check the accuracy of existing tables by calculating the differences and checking for irregularities in the final column of each table.

Babbage had the inspiration for the difference engine in 1812, but it was ten years before he was able to demonstrate even a simplified model. By this time, he had been elected a Fellow of the Royal Society, and this body helped him interest the government in backing the development of an advanced model that would produce tables of figures accurate to 20 decimal places. Unfortunately, designing the machine took Babbage much longer than he had anticipated, and the government eventually withdrew its support in 1842. Although a model of the difference engine was successfully used some 20 years later for calculating life insurance tables, there was no further development. By this time, Babbage had already become involved in a project to construct a much more ambitious calculating machine – the analytical engine.

left The remains of the difference engine, an elaborate machine designed in the 1800s by Charles Babbage for calculating mathematical data. He abandoned this device so that he could work on his even more complex analytical engine.

Analytical engine

Babbage aimed to achieve the then remarkable speed of one calculation per second and, to do this, had to find a way of speeding up the input of data. Manually turning wheels to set numbers took far too long. In 1833, Babbage announced his plan. No longer would written records have to be transferred to a machine by hand. Instead, the data would be recorded in code as patterns of holes punched in cards, which could be recognised by the machine. These cards formed what Babbage called the store. The mechanism for reading data from the cards and performing calculations was called the mill. The process was to be carried out automatically under instructions from another part of the machine called the control. And more punched cards were to store sets of instructions, so that the machine could be made to carry out different kinds of calculations.

Mathematician Ada Lovelace, daughter of poet Lord Byron and later to become Countess of Lovelace, collaborated with Babbage and demonstrated her deep understanding of the principles involved in the analytical engine. She wrote about programming and is credited with becoming the first computer programmer, having devised a set of instructions for the machine.

Sadly, the analytical engine was too complex to construct, but Babbage had laid the foundations for the development of electronic digital computers. There was nothing new in the use of punched cards to store data – a similar system was already used in some looms to determine the patterns woven into fabrics – and using toothed wheels to calculate was an even older idea. But his store, instructions and control corresponded to what we now refer to as the data, program and processor in today's electronic computers.

below right A portrait of American inventor Herman Hollerith, and one of the punched–card machines he built for automatically tabulating census results. It was used for the 1890 census, and greatly increased the speed of data processing.

below The German World War II Enigma machine was a precursor of modern computers. Although mechanical rather than digital, its complex system of interchangeable rotors and wiring made the writing of codes less laborious.

Logic and statistics

Another contributor to computer science was English mathematician George Boole, who based a form of symbolic logic on the processes of human thought. Logic, he said, was a matter for mathematicians rather than philosophers. With the appearance of his first publication on the subject, *Mathematical Analysis of Logic* (1847), the branch of mathematics now known as Boolean algebra was born. It is fundamental to the logical design of modern digital computers.

In the 1880s, American statistician Herman Hollerith developed electrically powered calculating machines that used data stored on punched cards. His main aim was to speed up the task of tabulating the results of the census. He was widely acclaimed when, in 1890, his machines were used to process the census data at three times the speed previously achieved . Hollerith machines soon became popular for various statistical tasks and, in 1896, he set up the Tabulating Machine Company to build his machines. In 1911, Hollerith sold his interest in the company. In 1924, this became International Business Machines Corporation (IBM).

With reliable electrically powered calculators now well established, and with the development of electronic vacuum tubes (valves), scientists and engineers could see ways of devising more powerful calculating machines. Babbage's ideas could be put into practice using relatively simple powered mechanisms for some tasks, such as handling punched cards and printing results, and electro-mechanical devices and valves for the more complex task of calculating.

Relay and valves

In Germany, Konrad Zuse developed a mechanical computer in 1936, then went on to produce three relay-operated machines. Relays are switches operated by electromagnets, and a series of relays can hold a number in coded form, according to which relays are in the on position and which are off. American George Stibitz, working for Bell Laboratories, completed their first relay computer in 1939 but, in that same year, American scientist John Atanasoff advanced computer technology when he introduced a semi-electronic digital computer. In this, some of the tasks previously performed by relays were carried out using valves. A small signal applied to an electrode called the grid would switch a valve from a conducting state to a non-conducting state, or vice-versa. So the valves acted as controlled switches, just like relays, but they could operate at much higher speeds and did not suffer from dirty contacts causing unreliable operation. However, valves did fail from time.

In collaboration with IBM, physicist Howard Aiken began work that same year at Harvard University on an advanced relay-operated machine. In those days, a powerful machine meant a large and expensive machine, and the idea of mass production was completely out of the question. Even so, it could not have been encouraging for Aiken when, in 1943, IBM chairman Thomas Watson declared: 'I think there is a world market for maybe five computers'.

During the final stages of development, a fault occurred, and computer scientist Grace Hopper discovered the cause – a moth had

above JW Mauchly with the ENIAC computer, Philadelphia 1946.

Digital computers handle data in binary (two-digit) form. This means that numbers are represented by a relatively long series of digits. For example, the decimal number 74 is 01001010 in binary. From the right, least significant position, this represents 0 x 1 plus 1 x 2 plus 0 x 4 plus 1 x 8 plus 0 x 16 plus 0 x 32 plus 1 x 64 plus 0 x 128. Whereas we find the decimal system more convenient, computers are easier to design and more reliable if they use the binary system, for each 1 or 0 can be represented by the presence or absence of an electrical voltage, so a number can be set up simply on a series of on-off switches. Large numbers of relays – switches operated by electromagnets – featured in computer designs developed in the 1930s. These relays could be operated by other circuits, thus enabling calculating processes to be carried out automatically. Modern computers use electronic memory devices as a temporary store for numbers and other data.

crawled into the machine and become jammed between the contacts of a relay. Forever afterwards, when something went wrong with the machine, she would say she was hunting for a bug, and that name for the cause of computer malfunction is still used today.

When completed in 1944, Aiken's huge machine, known as Harvard Mark I, was over 15 metres in length and about 2.5 metres high. Cards were used for data input, and the processing was controlled by a program fed in on punched paper tape. Results were provided in printed form, or on punched cards if the data had to undergo further processing.

Electronic computers

In February 1946, J Presper Eckert and John William Mauchly of the University of Pennsylvania produced the first all-electronic general-purpose digital computer. This machine, called ENIAC (Electronic Numerical Integrator and Computer), weighed nearly 30 tonnes, contained nearly 18,000 valves and consumed as much electricity as an electric fire with 150 bars. Being valve operated, it could calculate at up to 1,000 times as fast as contemporary relay-operated computers. ENIAC could carry out various kinds of calculation, although reprogramming the machine was a tedious business involving the soldering of wire connecting links. During testing, ENIAC had performed calculations for hydrogen-bomb development, and it was later used for other military purposes, including the calculation of shell trajectories for the artillery. It took 20 seconds to compute the 30 second trajectory of a shell, but it took programmers two days to set up the machine to perform this task. The construction of ENIAC marked the start of what we now call the first generation of computers – all-electronic valve operated machines.

Years later, legal action taken by John Atanasoff resulted in his gaining official recognition as the first person to build an electronic computer. However, although ENIAC did have some features in common with Atanasoff's computer, ENIAC was far superior, and historians generally continue to credit Eckert and Mauchly for their pioneering work.

Another first for the men from Pennsylvania came in 1949, when they introduced the use of magnetic tape for data storage in BINAC, their Binary Automatic Computer. Instead of storing data as patterns of holes on cards or paper tape, they used patterns of magnetic spots. This was more convenient for automatic handling, and had the advantage that the magnetic tape could be erased when required and then used to store new data.

Eckert and Mauchly's third machine was the Universal Automatic Computer, known as UNIVAC I, which appeared in 1951. This was intended for business applications, and the use of extra codes to represent letters and punctuation meant that it could handle text as well as numbers. The computer was still just a complicated calculator, but the ability to handle text would eventually enable it to become a multipurpose machine.

Electronic computers of the late 1940s held coded data internally in various ways involving the storage of electric charge. In one system, the electron beam in a cathode-ray tube was switched on and off rapidly to produce a pattern of charged spots on a fluorescent screen, which it scanned line by line, as in a television set. The charge pattern was

right ENIAC, the first all–electronic general–purpose digital computer, undergoing tests in Maryland, USA, in the mid-1940s. The machine, which weighed nearly 30 tonnes, was used by the US Army for calculations to do with bombs and shell trajectories.

continually refreshed before it had time to leak away. A mesh of wires on the outside of the tube was used to detect the stored data when required.

With computers becoming more complex and requiring greater internal storage capacity, a simpler and more compact technique was needed. This came in 1951 with the introduction of the magnetic core storage unit – a wire mesh with tiny magnetisable rings encircling the intersections. Circuits connected to the wires allowed the magnetic states of the cores to be set and read back when the data was needed.

Solid-state electronics

By this time, the best computers were equipped with the basic features that they have today, but were so much larger and much less powerful. However, an invention made in 1948 was to bring about a revolution in electronics. At Bell Laboratories, William Shockley, John Bardeen and Walter Brattain invented the transistor. This device, based on a tiny piece of the semiconductor silicon, could replace the valve in some electronic circuits. Besides being smaller than a valve, the transistor used relatively little power. It was also more robust and reliable, being a 'solid-state' device, as opposed to an assembly of parts in an evacuated glass envelope. For this important development, the three inventors received the Nobel Prize for Physics eight years later.

At first, transistors were used mainly in amplifiers; then they started to replace the valves in computer logic circuits, greatly reducing the space needed, the power requirements, and the heat generated. Breakdowns became much less frequent too. This change from valves to transistors marked the start of the second generation of computers. The first all-transistor computer was made in 1958 in the United States by a team at Control Data, headed by Seymour Cray. By that time, engineers Jack Kilby and John Noyce, working independently, were devising techniques for producing integrated circuits, advanced solid-state devices consisting of electronic circuits containing transistors and other components etched into tiny slices of silicon crystal. Such 'chips' were destined to change the face of computing, and the rest of the electronics industry too, for they would enable equipment to be made even more compact. Development was rapid and in 1961 Fairchild introduced the first commercially available integrated circuits, and these soon became incorporated in a wide range of electronic equipment, including computers.

With computers becoming ever smaller and somewhat cheaper, although still much too dear for the average person, Alan Keys, later to become a designer for Apple, suggested in 1969 that it might be worthwhile producing a personal computer.

In 1971 Intel produced the first microprocessor – a single-chip central processing unit for calculating devices. Although development was expensive, once a chip was in production, complex circuits could be reproduced at little cost. As a result, tiny pocket calculators consisting of a plastic keyboard, numeric display, one chip and little else, were marketed in their millions. And soon, more complex microprocessors were incorporated into a third generation of computers, reducing both size and cost, and paving the way for the introduction of the personal computer.

opposite The first programmable computer, called 'Baby', which ran its first program in June 1948. Tom Kilburn and Freddie Williams developed the machine at Manchester University, England. It had a total memory of just 1024 bits (binary digits).

below A magnified view of part of an integrated circuit (IC), consisting of numerous interconnected electronic components etched into a tiny chip of silicon. The use of ICs led to today's desktop PCs, which are far more powerful than the giant computers of just a few decades ago.

Getting personal

The first of the commercial personal computers, or microcomputers as they were usually called in those days, was the Altair 8800, made by MITS and launched in 1975. This was the idea of a former US Air Force officer called Ed Roberts. His calculator company had fallen on hard times, but he persuaded the bank to finance his new project, having told them he could sell 800 computers in a year. Within one month of the launch, orders for the machine were running at 250 per day.

The Altair 8800 was aimed, not at the general public, but at electronics enthusiasts, many of whom built their own machine from a kit ($395), although it was also sold assembled for $300 more. The Altair was more use for demonstrating a few basic principles of computer science than for performing useful tasks. There was no monitor or keyboard, and it had to be programmed by the laborious process of setting a row of switches to enter a few bits of code at a time. This was repeated many times and, if a mistake was made, the whole process had to be restarted. Once successfully programmed, the Altair 8800 could add a couple of numbers together and display the result in binary code on a row of lights. At that time, some people were fascinated by the fact that they could program an electronic circuit to calculate in the way they specified, but most people's attitude was 'so what?'. After all, a pocket calculator was simpler and more impressive to most people at that time.

One person who realised that the home computer would need software that could be loaded easily was Bill Gates. He persuaded programmer Paul Allen to cooperate in producing software to try out on the Altair. The success of this project led the two young men to form Microsoft – now the world's leading software company.

Steve Jobs and Steve Wozniac produced their first computer, Apple I, in 1976. This cost $666.66, and was a more capable machine than the Altair, although it was still aimed at the electronics hobbyist, and consisted only of a basic circuit board. The purchaser had to acquire and connect the keyboard and other parts. Only 50 of these computers were produced, and there was still no computer likely to interest the general public. In 1977, Ken Olsen, founding president of Digital Equipment Corporation, expressed the opinion that 'There is no reason for any individual to have a computer in their home.' It was certainly true that most people did not want to buy an expensive machine that could do so little, but things were about to change. Apple II was launched that year and was the first microcomputer aimed at the general public. It had a keyboard and floppy disk drive, and could even produce colour graphics. Demand was high, especially after the introduction of new software, which made the machines even more versatile. The most important of these was VisiCalc, introduced in 1978 by Dan Bricklin and Bob Frankston.

left The motherboard of Apple's first computer, which was built in 1976 by Steve Jobs and Stephen Wozniak. They produced only 50 boards, which sold for $666.66 each. Purchasers had to supply the keyboard and other necessary parts.

This first spreadsheet program attracted the attention of accountants. Large columns of numbers had to be added, and results carried from one column to another. If a change had to be made in the early part of a table of figures, most of the sheet would have to be recalculated. The computer could handle this task accurately and quickly, and accountants found that what had previously taken a week to work out could now be done in an hour or two, with accuracy. The introduction of word processing programs further boosted sales and, in 1980, hard magnetic disk drives became generally available for affordable mass storage of data and software.

IBM originally concentrated on large computers for businesses, but was impressed by the popularity of the microcomputer and introduced the IBM PC in 1981 at a cost over $2,500. IBM also allowed other firms to make compatible machines, whereas Apple kept the hardware market to themselves at that time. As a result, IBM compatible PCs eventually dominated the market.

right A molecular beam epitaxy unit for forming integrated circuits (ICs) on a slice of silicon crystal. The ICs are mass produced, and just one such 'silicon chip' may replace millions of conventional components at a small fraction of the cost.

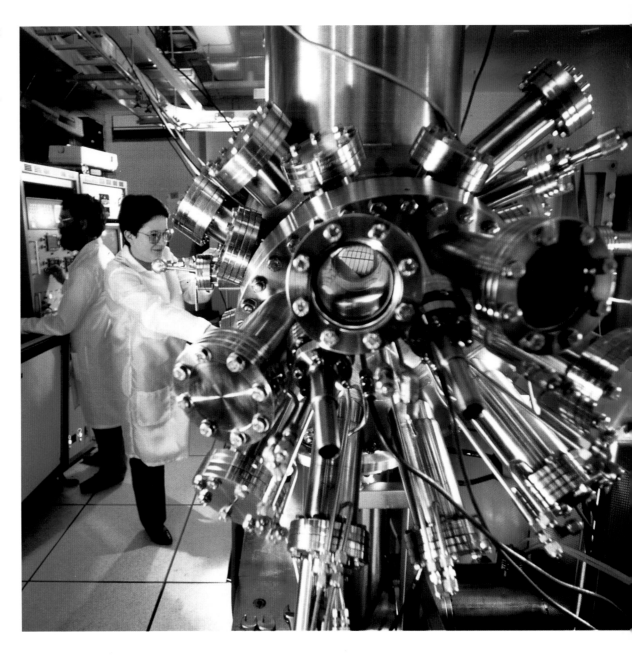

Graphical interface

In 1983, Apple introduced their Lisa computer, equipped with an extra input device – the mouse. Instead of typing characters on the keyboard to control the computer, many operations could be carried out by moving the mouse to direct a pointer across the screen and then pressing a button. At various stages, a list of options would appear on the screen, and the user had simply to 'point and click' in order to determine the next stage of operations. Sometimes, the options would be represented by graphics called icons, and this new facility that made using the computer so much easier became known as GUI – the graphical user interface. Sales of Lisa were poor, but Apple retained the GUI for their Macintosh range of computers, the first of which was launched in 1984. This proved highly successful, and, within a few years, Apple had become a major corporation, having grown faster than any other company in American history. Steve Jobs later reminisced that, at the age of 23 years, he was worth over one million dollars; at 24, over ten million; and, at 25, more than 100 million dollars.

Boom and bust

During the 1980s, production costs were falling rapidly, and numerous companies sprang up to provide cheap computers for the domestic market. To keep the price down, most of these machines used an ordinary television set as the monitor, and programs were commonly stored on audio cassettes. Many enthusiasts were children, using their computers for playing games or for writing their own programs in a simple computer language called BASIC – Beginners' All-purpose Symbolic Instruction Code. At first, these home computers had very little memory, so they could store only short, relatively simple programs with limited capabilities. However, many found a great deal of satisfaction in writing a program and getting it to work, even if it merely performed some mundane calculation that could more easily be done with pen and paper.

In the early years of the decade, there had been a great gulf between these simple machines and those aimed at small businesses, which needed more memory to run complex programs, and a high-quality monitor that could display text and figures clearly. But prices continued to fall and many firms producing budget-priced computers went out of business as more and more people switched to higher quality machines. By the end of the decade, with the range of available software ever widening, the personal computer could appeal to almost everyone, whatever their interests. The same machine could be used for games, education, graphics, word processing, and many other tasks, including exchanging information with other computers.

Originally, only the largest organisations could afford the luxury of a computer, but desktop computers had by now become common in offices, especially for word processing. IBM-compatible personal computers, generally known simply as PCs, were widely used. Numerous manufacturers competed for this market, and the competition led to large price cuts. Apple, however, had retained exclusive manufacturing rights to their Macintosh computers, or Macs, and had kept prices high. Many software companies had produced versions of their programs for both the PC and the Mac but, with so many more PCs around, it became more important commercially to concentrate on PC versions. Mac versions usually followed, but some software was produced for the PC only, and this helped the PC to get even further ahead as far as sales were concerned. However, for some applications, the Mac has proved its superiority and, to this day, it is the machine generally preferred by designers in magazine and illustrated book publishing.

right Book and magazine layouts, traditionally done using pen and paper, are now produced on a desktop computer running a page design program. Text from a word processor and images from a digital scanner (left of monitor) are later incorporated into the layout.

Networks

Computers can be linked together by cables to form a network for sending messages and sharing information. In large organisations, the network may provide links between all the staff in different buildings. Communications have always been vital to the defence of a country and, in 1969, the US Department of Defense required an infallable network for linking with university researchers and companies developing military equipment. The Advanced Research Project Fund was in charge of allocating money for research, so the network project became known as ARPAnet. The idea was for multiple links to be provided throughout the network so that, if an enemy destroyed part of it, communications would be automatically rerouted through other links. With a large number of alternative routes, it would be almost impossible for an enemy to disrupt communications completely. The system was set up and, in 1972, carried the first E-mail message. England and Norway were linked to ARPAnet in 1973, thus making it an international network.

By 1983, ARPAnet was being used so heavily by university staff that the Department of Defense set up Milnet – a new network for military use only. However, it would be possible to communicate with those on the ARPAnet when required using software to establish communications links. In 1984, the US National Science Foundation started to organise many more links to enable inter-network communications.

At first, people at universities were the main users as they had ready access to computers and networks. The home computer enthusiast was usually restricted to using the telephone system in order to connect to a bulletin board, a computer on which messages could be left for other callers to read and respond to. Many companies used computer communications mainly for internal messages, although some publishers were finding it useful to be able to send text to printing firms over a telephone line or dedicated private cable.

above With a virtual reality headset connected to a computer, movement of the head changes the view seen, just as in real life. Besides miniature screens for 3D vision, the headset also has earphones for stereophonic sound. The aim is to make an artificial environment seem as real as possible.

above right NASA's home (introductory) page on the World Wide Web. The Web is the main information service provided by the Internet, which is a global system of interconnected computer networks. The Internet also provides E-mail and other electronic message facilities.

below right The Internet allows anyone with a computer and a connection access to millions of other users all over the world. Sending E-mail is as simple as dialling a number, accessing the network and transmitting your message.

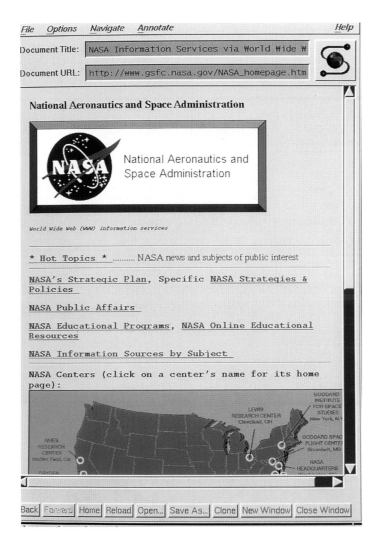

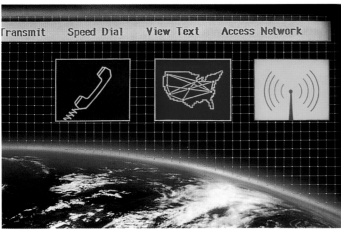

The Internet

Everything changed after 1990, when communications expert Tim Berners-Lee showed how interconnected networks could be expanded indefinitely, with access for all. The Internet was born! By 1995, there were improved international communications links, and relatively cheap modems – devices needed to connect computers to the telephone system. Tens of millions of people were now connected to the Internet, and could send E-mail around the world for the price of a local call to their Internet service provider. Newsgroups had been formed on the Internet for open discussion about almost any subject, and companies established sites to display their products and services on the part known as the world wide web.

Today, the number of people using the Internet continues to grow. 'Virtual communities' become established when people find a place on the Internet where they can discuss a common interest. As in a local pub, many participants in the discussions are regulars, and you get to know whose opinions you want and whose you don't. The main difference is that, on the Internet, the people you communicate with may live anywhere in the world. Perhaps this is the most important aspect of the Internet – the way in which it encourages international communications and, with luck, a better understanding of other ways of life.

index

Page numbers in italics refer to illustrations.

abacuses 172
achromatic lenses 77, 131
Advanced Research Project Fund 186
aerial bombardment 144
aeroplanes *see* airplanes
Agricultural Revolution 51
agriculture 49-54
Aiken, Howard 177
airplanes 69, *69*, *71*
airships 68
Alcock, Walter 117
Aldrin, Edwin *82*, 83
Allbutt, Thomas 132
Allen, Paul 182
Altair 8000 182
altimeters, pressure 87
Ampère, André 150
anaesthetics 131
analytical engine 176
animals, domesticated 49
Apple 183, 184
Apple I 182
Apple II 182
aqueducts *32*, *33*
Arago, Dominque 150
Archer, Frederick Scott 105
arches 32
Argand, Aimé 112
Aristarchus of Samos 74
Aristotle 74
Arkwright, Richard 42, 43
Arlandes, Marquis d' 68
Armstrong, Neil 83
ARPAnet 186
aseptic surgery 131-132
astronomy 74-75
Atanasoff, John 177, 178
atlatls 138
atomic bombs 145
autogyros 71
automatic firearms 142
Avery, William 13, 64
aviation 68-71
Ayrton 163, 164

Babbage, Charles 174, *174*, 176
'Baby' (computer) *180*
Baekeland, Leo 26
Bain, Alexander 164
Baird, John Logie 165, 166, *166*, 168
Bakelite 26
Bakewell, Robert 52
ball-point pens 95
balloons 68
Bardeen, John 181
barometers *87*
Barthélémy 165
BBC see British Broadcasting
    Corporation
Bell, Alexander Graham 121, 151,
    151, 152, 153
Bell, Patrick 51
Benz, Karl 59, *59*
Berger, Hans 135
Berliner, Emile 122, 153
Berners-Lee, Tim 187
Bessemer, Henry 22
bicycles 58
Biro, Lazlo 95
black powder 141, 143
Blazer *151*
Blenkinsop, John 66, 67
blowguns 139
blowpipes 139
boats 63
Bodley, George 115
bombs 144-145
Bonaparte, Napoleon 148
Boole, George 177
Boolean algebra 177
Bouchon, Basil 44
Boulton, Matthew 13
bows 139
Boyle, Robert 114
Brahms, Johannes 121
Bramah, Joseph 116, *116*
Branley, Edouard 155
Brattain, Walter 181
Braun, Karl Ferdinand 159, 165

Braun, Wernher von 83, *144*
breech loading cartridges 142
breeding, intensive 52
Brewster, David 105
Bricklin, Dan 182
bricks 31, 32, 34
bridges 36-37, *37*
British Broadcasting Company 160
British Broadcasting Corporation
    (BBC) 160, 166, 167
bronze 21
Bronze Age 21
bronze tools 31
Brunel, Isambard Kingdom 64, *64*
BSkyB's playout centre *168*
building 31-37
Bushnell, David 63

Caesar, Julius 89, 148
calculators, mechanical 172,
    173
calendars 89
calotypes 104
camera obscura 102, *103*
cameras *107*, 108
carbon transmitters 153
Carré, Ferdinand 117
cars 59-60, *59*, *61*
Cartwright, Edmund 43
Cassegrain, N 77
catapults 138-139
cathode-ray tubes 165
Cayley, George 69
celluloid 26
Chappe, Claude 148
chariot *58*
Charles, Jacques 68
Chemical News 163
Chinese writing 94
chips, silicon 181, *181*
chromatic aberration 77

Cierva, Juan de la 71
cinema 107-108
clinical thermometers 132
clocks 90
clothing 41
coal 14
coal gas 15
coal processing plant *14*
Cockerell, Christopher 65
coherers 155, 156
Coke, Thomas 52
collodion system 105
colour photography 105-106
colour television systems 168
colours, textiles 44
Colt, Samuel 142
combine harvesters *52*, 53
communications 148-169
compound microscopes 131
computerized axial tomography
    135
computers 172-187
concrete 32
    reinforced 34
construction 31-37
Conte, Jaques 94
Cooke, William 150
cookers 115
cooking 115
cooling 115, 117
Copernicus, Nicolaus 75, *75*, 76
copper 20-21
cotton harvesting *43*
Cray, Seymour 181
Crompton, Samuel 42
Crookes, William 162, 163, *163*
Crookes tubes *162*
crop rotation 51, 52
crossbows 139
crystal sets 159, 160
cubit 86
Cugnot, Nicholas-Joseph 58
Cullen, William 115
cycling 58

daggers 138
Daguerre, Louis 104
daguerrotype process 104
Daily Mail 160
Daimler, Gottlieb 58, 59
Davy, Humphry 14, *14*, 113, 131
De Forest Wireless Telegraph
    Company 159
De Forest Wireless Telephone
    Company 159
Diamond Sutra *95*
Dickson, William 108
Diesel, Rudolf 60
diesel engines 60, *60*, 65, 67
difference engine 174, *175*
digital computers 172-187
digital recording 125
digital signalling 148
diode valves 159
discs, recording 122
distance 87
Dolby noise reduction systems 124
domestic appliances 112-117
Doppler, Christian 79
Doppler effect 79
Drais, Karl von 58
Drake, Edwin 16
drawlooms 44
Drebbel, Cornelius 63
Drexler, Eric 27
Drinker, Philip 135
dry plates, photography 105
Duddell, William 158
dyers market, Fez *45*
dyes 44
dynamite 143

e-mail 187
ear trumpet *132*
Eastman, George 105, *105*
Eckert, J Presper 178
    Edison, Thomas Alva 20, 108,
114, 121, *121*, 153, 159
Einstein, Albert 17, 145
Einthoven, Willem 135
electric lighting 113-114
electric rail transport 67
electric shocks 132
electric telegraph systems 148-151
electric vehicles 60
electric vision 163
electricity 17, 113
electrocardiograph 135
electroencephalographs 135
electromagnetic induction 152
electromagnetism 113, 150

electromagnets 150
electron microscopes 135
electronic scanning systems 167
energy 8-17
engines
    internal combustion *16*, 58-60,
        60, 65, 67
    micro *27*
    steam *12*, 13
English longbows 139
ENIAC (Electronic Numerical
Integrator and Computer) *177*, 178,
    179
Enigma machine *176*
equal-arm balances 88
Ericsson, John 64
explosives 141, 143-144

facsimile machines 164
factory farming 54
Faraday, Michael *15*, 113, 152
farming 49-54
Fermi, Enrico 17
Fessenden, R A 158, 159
Feynman, Richard 27
field radio set *161*
film dubbing studio *125*
fire 8, 49, 112
fire power 139, 141
firearms, automatic 142
firing mechanisms 141
fishing 55
Fitch, John 63
Fitton, Henry 107
Fleming, John Ambrose *158*, 159
Fletcher, Harvey 123
flintlocks 141
flying shuttles 41
food 49
Ford, Henry 60
Forest, Lee De 159, *159*, 160, 165
Forlanini, Enrico 65
Forsyth, John 141
fountain pens 94
Frankston, Bob 182
Fraunhofer, Joseph von 79

Gagarin, Yuri *82*
Galen of Pergamum 128
Galilei, Galileo 76, *76*, 90
Galvani, Luigi 113
galvanometers 135
gas, natural 15-16

gas lighting 113
Gates, Bill 182
Gatling, Richard 142
Geissler, Heinrich 162
Geissler tube *162*
Genghis Khan 148
Gibbon, John 135
Giffard, Henri 68
glass 24
Glidden, Carlos 98
gliders 69
Global Positioning System (GPS) *90*
Goddard, Robert 80, *80*, 81
Goodyear, Charles 22
Goubert, Claude-Desiré 63, 64
GPS *see* Global Positioning System
gramophone records 122, *122*
gramophones 122-123
graphical user interface (GUI) 184
gravure printing 97-98
Gray, Frank 168
Great Eastern *64*
'Greek fire' 141
Gregorian calender 89
Gregory, James 77
Gregory XIII, Pope 89
grenades 143
Gresley, Nigel 67
GUI *see* graphical user interface
guided missiles 144
guncotton 143
gunpowder 141
guns 141-142
Gutenberg, Johann 97, *97*
Gutenberg Bible *96*

halberds 138
Hall, Chester Moor 77, 131
Hancock, Thomas 22
Hargreaves, James 42
Harington, John 117
Harrison, John 89, *89*, 90
Harvard Mark I 178
harvesting machines 53
Harvey, William 128
heart pacemakers 135
heart transplants 135
heart-lung machines 135, *135*
heating 115
Hedley, William 67
helicopters *70*, 71
Helmholtz, Hermann von 132
Hennebique, François 34
Hero of Alexandria 13
Hertz, Heinrich 155, 163
hi-fi 123

hieroglyphics *93*
high-fidelity records 123
Hiroshima, August 1945: *137*
hiss, eliminating in recordings
    124-125
Hollerith, Herman *176*, 177
Hooke, Robert 90
Hopper, Grace 177
horses 51, 66
hot-air balloons 68, *68*
hot metal machines 98
hovercraft 65
Hubble space telescope *73*
Hunnings, Henry 153
Huygens, Christiaan *88*, 90, 114
Hyatt, John 26
hydrofoils 65
hydrogen balloons 68
hydrogen bombs 145
hypodermic syringes 132

IBM *see* International Business
Machines Corporation
IBM PCs 183
immunology 131
incandescent lamps 114
inoculation 131
instant pictures 106
integrated circuits 181, *181*
interlaced scanning 169
internal combustion engines *16*,
    58-60
International Business Machines
    Corporation (IBM) 177, 183
International Space Station *83*
Internet 187
iron 21-22, 34, 35
Iron Age 21
iron lung machines 135

Jacquard, Joseph Marie 44
Jansky, Karl 79
Janssen, Zacharias *130*, 131
Jazz Singer 108, *109*
Jenner, Edward 131
jet aircraft 71
Jobs, Steve 182, 184

Kay, John 41, *41*
Kelly, William 22

Keys, Alan 181
kidney transplants 135
Kilburn, Tom 181
Kilby, Jack 181
Kinetoscope *108*
Klic, Karl 98
Korn, Arthur 164
Kurobe Dam, Toyama *10*

Laënnec, René 132
lances 138
Land, Edwin H 106
Lanston, Tolbert 99
Lawson, H J 58
Lee, Edmund 11
Leeuwenhoek, Anton van 131
Leibnitz, Gottfried 172
length 86-87
Lenoir, Etienne 59
Leonarda da Vinci 69, 128
letterpress 97
lifts, safety hoist 35
lighting 112-114
Lights of New York 108
Lilienthal, Otto 69
line standards, television 169
Lippershey, Hans 76
Lisa (computer) 184
Lister, Joseph 131, 132
lithography 97
locomotives 66-67, *66*, *67*
Lodge, Oliver 155, 156
logic 177
Long, Crawford 131
long-playing records 123
longbows 139
looms *42*, 43-44, *44*
Lovelace, Ada 176
LPs 123
Lumière, Auguste and Louis 106, 108

machine guns 142
machines 8, 10
Macintosh, Charles 22
Macintosh computers 184
Macmillan, Kirkpatrick 58
Macs see Macintosh computers
Maddox, Richard 105
maglev trains 65, *67*
magnetic core storage units 181
magnetic resonance imaging 135

magnetic tape 178
Mallard steam locomotive *67*
Marconi, Guglielmo *154*, 155, 156, 157
Marconi Company 160
Marey, Etienne-Jules 108
mass (weight) 87-88
matches 112
materials 20-27
    writing 94
Mathematical Analysis of Logic 177
Mauchly, John William *177*, 178
Maudslay, Henry 116
Maxim, Hiram Stevens 140, *140*, 142
Maxim gun *140*
Maxwell, James Clerk 105, 155
May, Louis 163
McAdam, John 36
McCormick, Cyrus 51, 53
meals, packaged *54*
measurements 86-90
mechanical calculators 172, *173*
mechanical scanning systems 166
mechanization, agriculture 52-53
medical technology 128-135
Melba, Nellie 160
Melville, Alexander 151
Mergenthaler, Ottmar 99
Merkle, Ralph 27
metallographic printing 97
metre 86
Michaux, Pierre 58
microcomputers 182
microengines *27*
microprocessors 181
microscopes 131, 135
Microsoft 182
milking parlour *53*
Milnet 186
miner's safety lamps 14, *14*
missiles, guided 144
mixing desk, recording studio *119*
mobile phones *153*
modern techniques, agriculture 54
modulation 158
molecular beam epitaxy unit *183*
Monier, Joseph 34
Monroe, William 94
Montgolfier, Joseph-Michel and Jacques-Etienne 68
Morse, Samuel 150
Morse telegraph receiver *148*
Morton, William 131
motherboard, Apple computer *182*
mouse (computer) 184
moving pictures 107-108
mud huts, Buniamin *31*
Muggeridge, Edward see Muybridge, Eadweard

mules (machine) 42-43
multistage steam turbines 65
multitrack tape machines 124
Murdock, William 13
Muybridge, Eadweard 107
muzzle-loaders 141

nanotechnology 27
natural gas 15-16
negative-positive system, photography 104
networks 186
neutron bombs 145
New Horse Houghing Husbandry 50
Newcomen, Thomas 12, 13
Newton, Isaac 77
Niepce, Nicéphore 102, *102*, 104
Nipkow, Paul 163, 164
nitroglycerine 143
Nobel, Alfred 143
Noble experyence of the vertuous handy warke of surgeri 128
Noyce, John 181
nuclear energy 17
nuclear fission 17
nuclear power station, Chooz *17*
nuclear-powered vessels 65

Oakley, Annie 139
Oberth, Hermann 83
Oehmichen, Etienne 71
Oersted, Hans Christian 113, 150
offset litho machines 99
oil 15-16
oil lamps 112
oil production platform *15*
Olsen, Ken 182
operating theatre *134*
ophthalmoscopes 132
Otis, Elisha *34*, 35

palmtop computers *153*
Papin, Denis 13, 114, *114*
paraffin lamps *112*, *113*
Parkes, Alexander 26
Parkesine 26
Parsons, Charles 64
Pascal, Blaise 172, *173*
pattern weaving 44

PCs see personal computers
pencils 94
pendulum-regulated clocks 90
pens 94, 95
percussion firing 141
Perkin, William 44
Perry 163, 164
personal computers 182, 184
petrol engines 59, 60
phenakistoscopes 107, *107*
phonographs *120*, 121, *121*
photography 102-106, *104*, *106*
pikes 138
pistols *138*
Pitts, Hiram and John 52
plastics 26
ploughing, steam-powered *52*
poisons 139
Polaroid Land camera 106
Poncelet, Jean-Victor 10
porcelain workshop, Sèvres *25*
Porta, Giovanni Battista della 102
Poulson, Valdemar 124, 158
Pravaz, Gabriel 132
Preece, William 156
pressure altimeters 87
pressure cookers 13
Priestley, Joseph 22
printed patterns, textiles 45
printing 95-99
Pritchard, Thomas 37
projectors *101*, 108
propellers 63-64
Ptolemy 75
punched cards 176
pyramids, Giza *30*
Pyrex glass 78

radar 87
radio astronomy 79
Radio Corporation of America (RCA) 167
radio telephony 157-159
radio telescopes 79
radio transmitting site, Rio *147*
railways 36, 66-67
RCA see Radio Corporation of America
reapers *51*
Reber, Grote 79
recording suite, radio station *161*
records (sound) 122, *122*, 123
rectifiers 159
reel-to-reel tape recorder *124*
reflecting telescopes 77

refracting telescopes 76, 77
refrigerators 115, *115*, 117
reinforced concrete 34
relay communication systems 148
relays 177
rifles, repeating *139*, 142
rifling 142
roads 36, *36*, *57*
Roberts, Ed 182
robotic welding machines *21*, *61*
Roci, Scipione 132
rockets 80, *80*, *81*, 83
Roentgen, Wihelm 133, *133*, 135
roll film 105
Roman agriculture 51
Roman calender 89
Roosevelt, Franklin 145
Rosing, Boris 165
Rozier, Jean Pilâtre de 68
rubber 22

sails 11, 63
satellites 83, *169*
Savery, Thomas 13
scanning 163-165, 166, 167, 169
Schoenberg, Isaac 166, 167
Schrötter, Anton von 112
Schulze, Johann 102
seed drills *50*, 51
semaphore telegraph 148, *149*
Senefelder, Alois 97
serpentines 141
sewing machines 117
sextants *86*
Shaw, Louis 135
ships 63
Shockley, William 181
Shoenbein, Christian 143
Sholes, Christopher 98
SI (Système International d'Unités) 90
Sikorsky, Igor Ivanovich 70, *70*
Singer, Isaac 117
Sivrae, Compte de 58
skyscrapers *34*, *35*, 36
slings 138
Smeaton, John 10, 13
smelting 21
Smith, Willoughby 163
Sobrero, Ascanio 143
software 182
sonar systems 55, *55*
Sony Walkman *124*
Sosigenes 89
Soulé, Samuel 98

sound recording 121-125
Sovereign of the Sea 65
space exploration 80, 83
space shuttle *Columbia 81*
sparks 112
spear throwers 138
spears 138
spectographs 79
speech transmission 158
sphygmomanometers 132
spinning 41
spinning frames 42
spinning jennys 41-42
spinning wheels 41
spring balances 88
Starley, James 58
Staudinger, Hermann 26
stealth planes *71*
steam carriages 58
steam engines *12*, 13
steam locomotives 66-67
steam power 13
steam traction engines 53
steam turbines 13, *13*, 64-65
steamships 63
steel 22
steel mill, continuous-casting *20*
stereophonic sound 123
stereoscopes 105
stethoscopes 132
Stevenson, George 67
Stevin, Simon 58
Stibitz, George 177
sticks 138
stone 31-32
Sturgeon, William 150
submarines 63, *63*, 64
sun *76*
sundials *85*, 89
surgery, aseptic 131-132
Sutton, Thomas 105
Swan, Joseph 114
Swinton, A A Campbell 165, 166
swords 138
syringes, hypodermic 132
Système International d'Unités (SI) 90

Tabulating Machine Company 177
Talbot, William Fox 104
talking pictures 108
tanks *143*, *145*
tape machines, multitrack 124
tape recording 124

Tawell, John 150
telegraph systems 148-151
telegraphones 124
telephone exchanges *152*
telephones 151-153, *151*, *153*
telescopes 76-80, *78*, *79*
television 163-169
television factory *167*
television studio *168*
Telford, Thomas 36, 37
Tennyson, Lord 121
textile printing 45
thaumatropes 107
thermometers, clinical 132
Thomson, J J 163
throwing sticks 138
time 89-90
Townshend, Charles 52
tractors 53
trams 60
transistors 181
transmitters, carbon 153
transplants 135
transport 58-71
trepanning 128
trephining 128
Trevithick, Richard 66, *66*
triode valves 160, *165*
Tsiolkovski, Konstantin 80
Tull, Jethro 50, *50*, 51
tuning, wireless 156-157
tunnels 37
turbines 64
typewriters *98*

ultrasound scans 135, *135*
underwater craft 63
UNIVAC I (Universal Automatic Computer) 178

V-1 flying bombs 145
V-2 rocket-powered missiles *144*, 145
vaccines 131
vacuum cleaners *111*, 117, *117*
Vail, Alfred 150
Valensi, Georges 168
valves 177
Vaucanson, Jacques de 44
Vernier, Pierre 87
Vernier callipers 87
Vesalius, Andreas 128
video recorders 125

Vidie, Lucien 87
virtual reality headset *186*
visual telegraph 148, *149*
VLA (Very Large Array) radio telescope, Socorro *79*
Volta, Alessandro 113, 148
vulcanization 22

Walker, John 112
Waller, Augustus 132
water closets *116*, 117
water power 10
Waterman, L E 95
waterwheels 10, *10*, 51
Watson 153
Watson, Thomas 177
Watt, James *12*, 13
weapons 138-145
weaving 41, 43
weighing instruments 88
Welsbach, Baron von 113
Wheatstone, Charles 105, 150
Wheatstone and Cooke telegraph 150, *150*
wheels 58
White, Anthony 153
Whittle, Frank 71
Williams, Freddie 181
Winchester, Oliver 142
wind farms *11*
wind power 11
windmills 11, 51
Winsor, F A 15
wireless communications 155-160
wireless telegraphy 155
Wireless World *156*
Wozniac, Steve 182
Wren, Christopher 32
Wright, Wilbur and Orville 69, *69*
writing 94-95

X-ray equipment *133*
X-rays 133, *133*
Xylonite 26

Zeppelin, Count Ferdinand von 68
Zuse, Konrad 177
Zworykin, Vladimir Kosma 164, *164*, 167, 168

Photographic credits

Executive Editor **Mike Evans**
Editor **Humaira Husain**

Creative Director **Keith Martin**
Art Editor **Geoff Fennell**
Designer **Martin Topping**

Picture Research **Zoë Holtermann**
Production Controller **Joanna Walker**

First published in 1999 by **Hamlyn** an imprint of
Octopus Publishing Group Limited, 2-4 Heron Quays, London E14 4JP

© Octopus Publishing Group Limited 1999

A catalogue record for this book is available from the British Library
ISBN 0 600 59675 3

Produced by Toppan Printing Co Ltd
Printed in China

Agfa-Gevaert Ltd 107 top.
AKG, London 4 bottom right, 44, 59 left, 60, 68, 75 right, 82 left, 97, 102 top, 102 centre left, 105, 121, 122, 130 left, 137, 143, 152, 157, 173, 176 right, /AP 142, /Erich Lessing 32, 40, 48, /Jean-Louis Nou 91 top left.
AMS Neve PLC 125.
Art Directors & Trip Photo Library/A Miles 37 top, /H Rogers 4 bottom centre left, 45 left, 93.
Christie's Images Ltd 138, 139.
Corbis UK Ltd/James L. Amos 86, /Bettmann 76 left, 112-113, 177, /Joseph Sohm; ChromoSohm Inc. 5 centre right, 85, /Jerry Cooke 179, /Angelo Hornak 31, /Hulton Deutsch Collection 25, 42, 78, 167, /Robert Landau 109 bottom, /Larry Lee 30, /Charles E. Rotkin 13, 23, /Schenectady Museum; Hall of Electricity Foundation 10 left.
©DAL, Drake Automation 168 Bottom.
Dyson Appliances Ltd 5 bottom centre left, 111, 117.
Mary Evans Picture Library 12 left, 12 right, 14 top, 17 top left, 24 top, 50 left, 58, 59 right, 61 top, 66 left, 69 left, 69 right, 74, 75 left, 76 right, 88, 89 bottom, 96, 103, 107 bottom, 108, 109 top, 120, 132, 133 left, 140 bottom, 144 right, 148, 149, 151 left, 154, 161 left, 166, 174, /Institution of Civil Engineers 64 left.
Image Bank 9, 114 bottom, 168 top, /Ross. M. Horowitz front cover bottom centre, /Kaz Mori 34 top right, /Pascal Perret 5 bottom left, 147, /J.F. Podevin 187 bottom, /Terje Rakke 65, /D Redfearn front cover top, /Frank Whitney 5 centre left, 73, Institution Of Mechanical Engineers 70 bottom, 116 top, 116 bottom.
Nokia Mobile Phones 153.
Oxford Scientific Films/Kim Westerskov 55 right.
Redferns/Andrew Cepley 124 Bottom, /Mick Hutson 5 bottom centre right, 119 /David Redfern 123.
The Ronald Grant Archive 4 bottom centre right, 101.
The Royal Photographic Society, Bath, England 106.
Sandia National Laboratories /Courtesy of Sandia National Laboratories, Intelligent Micromachine Initiative;www.mdl.sandia.gov/Micromachine. 27 top, 27 bottom.
Science Photo Library 4 top left, 7, 50 right, 52 bottom, 70 top, 77, 94, 128, 129, 133 right, 140 top, 144 left, 151 right, 158, 159, 163, 164, 165, /Mike Agliolo 169, /AT & T Bell Labs 183, /George Bernard 62, /Jeremy Burgess 63, /Jean-Loup Charmet 162, /Tony Craddock back cover left, /Adam Hart-Davis 175, /Thomas Dodge/Agstock 52 top, /Michael Donne 135 top, /Francois Gohier 79, /James King-Holmes 4 centre left, 14 bottom, 47, 180, 186, /Albert Berenguier, Jerrican 33, /Gripe, Jerrican 55 left, /Peter Menzel 182, /Astrid & Hans Frieder Michler 181, /NASA back cover right, 80, 83, /Pascal Nieto, Jerrican 99 top, /Novosti 82 right, /David Parker 91 right, 187 top, /Alfred Paseika front endpaper, back endpaper, 1, 2-3, /Alfred Pasieka front cover bottom, /Science Pictures Ltd 99 bottom, /Rosenfeld Images Ltd 21, 45 right, /Victor De Schwanberg 24 bottom, /Volker Steger 176 left, /Taheshi Takahara 67 right, /Sheila Terry/ Rutherford Appleton Laboratory 5 bottom right, 171, /Geoff Tomkinson 19, /Geoff Tompkinson 4 Top Right, 26, /Ed Young/Agstock 43 bottom right.
Science & Society Picture Library/NMPFT 104, /National Railway Museum 66 right, 67 top left, /Science Museum 16, 34 bottom left, 41, 51, 64 right, 87, 89 top, 98, 114 top, 150, 156.
Sony Uk Ltd 124 top.
Tony Stone Images/Glen Allison front cover top centre, 11, /Ken Biggs 4 centre right, 57, /Tim Brown 135 bottom, /Sylvain Coffie 17 bottom right, /Pascal Crapet 36 top, /Peter Dean 53, /Lonnie Duka 161 right, /Tim Flach 185, /Jean Claude Grelier 134, /David Higgs 145, /Ross Harrison Koty 71, /Mark A. Leman 15, /John Lund 54, /Chris McCooey 10 right, /Jon Ortner 35, /Bertrand Rieger 5 top right, 39, /Warren Rosenberg 4 bottom left, 127, 130 right, /Andy Sacks 61 bottom, /Mark Segal 36 bottom, /Joseph Sohm 5 top left, 29, /Charles Thatcher 20, /Roger Tully 43 top left, /World Perspectives 81, /Eric K. K. Yu 37 bottom.
Werner Forman Archive/British Library, London 95.
Zanussi 115.

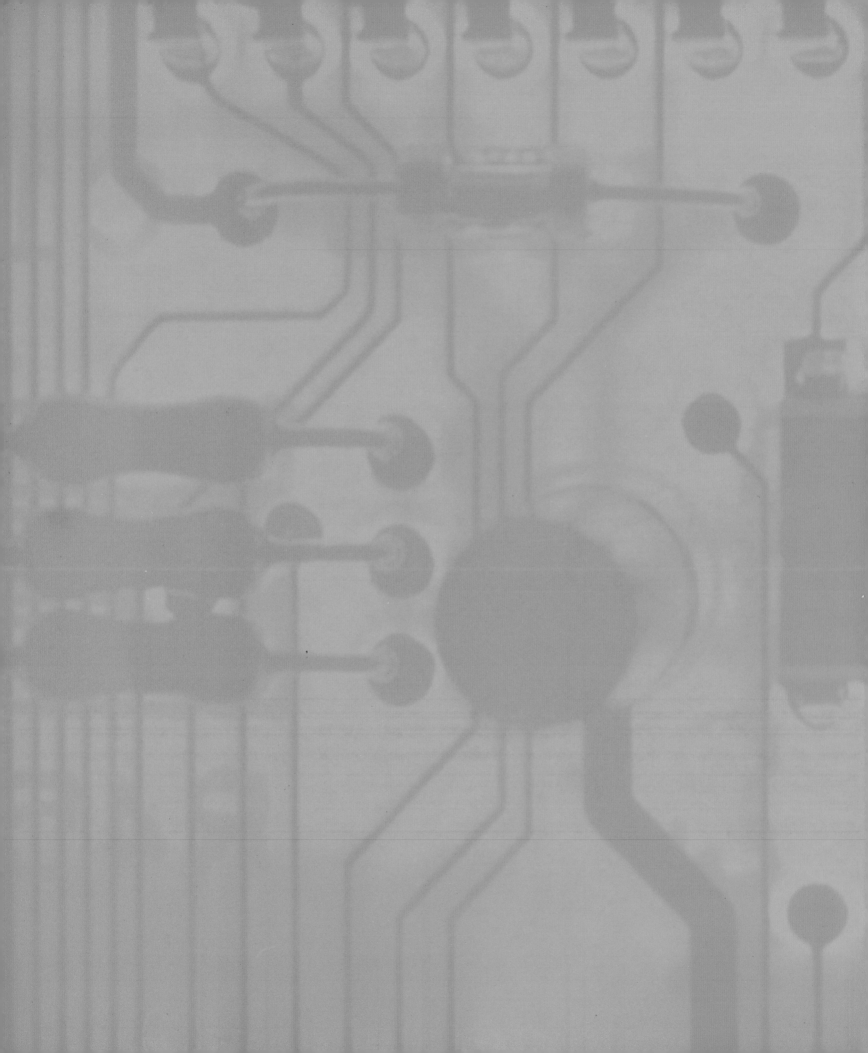